licensing rights in technology

a legal guide for managers in negotiation

G A BLOXAM

Gower Press

First published in Great Britain by Gower Press Limited
140 Great Portland Street, London W1N 5TA
1972

SBN 7161 0079 7

Set in 10 on 12 point Century
by The Pentagon Bureau
Printed in Hong Kong by
The Continental Printing Company

Contents

Preface

This book has been written to fill three significant gaps in the existing literature. The first, which is explained more fully in the Introduction, is the apparent absence of a book which explained to the manager, in depth *but using his own frame of reference and terminology*, the legal concepts involved in the licensing of industrial property.

The second gap which appears to exist is probably commonplace in literature explaining specialised subjects to non-specialists. To be of any use to the manager, a book on licensing must be based on the practical realities of everyday business life. The people who know about such things are the ones who are actually involved, but they in general have neither the time nor the inclination to develop the sort of argument which is the subject of this book. In brief, it requires a rather theoretical or academic approach to real-life experience, and in so far as I have succeeded in this approach I believe the book will fill the second of the two gaps. There is, however, an inherent limitation: while I have sought to base my generalisations fairly on experience, the experience must necessarily be my own. It follows that in the specific illustrations that I give from time to time the reader will detect a bias towards industrial chemistry as against other fields of technology.

Since so much of the book involves the interaction of different disciplines and their experts with each other and with the businessman/manager, I have had to express views on these interactions which may in some cases appear unconventional, controversial or even, occasionally, unpalatable. I believe readers will accept these views in the spirit in which they are intended — that of objective inquiry. It may, indeed, be no bad thing to introduce the occasional note of controversy or even provocation as a corrective for the atmosphere of conformism and agreement which tend to surround the organisation man to whom this book is mainly addressed.

A feature of the book which I believe will be valuable to non-American readers — and possibly of interest to American readers — is the section of Chapter 5 on US anti-trust law. Non-American businessmen often feel at a disadvantage when negotiating with Americans, since the cry of "anti-trust" which is frequently raised is liable to be taken as a ploy by the American to get his way on a negotiating issue. It is hoped that the section on anti trust law will enable the non-American to *understand* in general terms what is involved in anti-trust law and so to make a realistic approach to the negotiations, part of which will be a better grasp of his American opposite number's real difficulties and preoccupations with anti-trust.

I believe the anti-trust section has gained immeasurably from the valuable and extensive assistance given to me by Mr Herbert H Goodman, Patent Attorney. I am also greatly indebted to professional colleagues who wish to remain anonymous, for helping me in the section of Chapter 5 on Common Market law; to Mr Donald F Sim, QC of Toronto, Messrs Soga & Co of Tokyo and Messrs Remfry & Son of Calcutta for commenting on the sections in Chapter 5 dealing with their respective countries; and to a solicitor, who wishes to remain anonymous for professional reasons, for extensive help on the section of the same chapter on restraints on licensing in the UK which are due to non-patent statutes. Finally I wish to express my sincere thanks to my colleagues, Mr D R Springelt, FCA, for helping me with the section in Chapter 6 on taxation and Mr J R Bromley with the section of Chapter 5 on the communist countries and Dr M B Clark with Chapter 3.

The third gap in the literature which this book is intended to fill is that arising from the contradiction between the international function of licensing and the national character of the law. Licensing and technology are very much international affairs but law, especially (though paradoxically) the law of industrial property, is a stronghold of the nation-state ideology. Any author must write from the point of view of his own country. It seems to me that it is best to stand firmly on one's home ground but to make sure that any matters peculiar to the law applicable there are drawn to the attention of the reader, and where possible their foreign counterparts are given. That is the approach I have adopted.

While the book is primarily addressed to managers, I believe that practitioners, such as patent agents and lawyers concerned with licensing, may find the book interesting and even useful as a reflection in a practitioner's mind of the sort of help the manager is hoping (albeit often unconsciously) to get from the practitioner.

Introduction

The licensing of industrial property lies at the meeting point of a number of disciplines. Industrial property (the meaning and origin of this egregious term are developed in Chapter 1) is constituted by the legal rights arising from the fruits of a man's brain, in so far as they have industrial significance. Its nature is therefore a function of the technology concerned and the applicable law. Such rights can be made the subject of licences on terms set out in licence agreements; these are part of the law of contract. It follows that in terms of recognised qualifications, the licensing of industrial property involves expertise in the relevant branch of science or engineering; in industrial property law; and in contract law. In terms of people this means (in UK terminology) the scientist or engineer, the patent agent and the lawyer (solicitor or barrister). It would be extremely rare for the three disciplines to be practised by one man. Not only this, but the disciplines of technology and the law are remote from each other in outlook and method. The rules of the law are derived by deductive reasoning from existing statutes, and past precedents and authority; the rules of science by inductive reasoning from observation. Thus a rule of law stands until and unless it is overturned by new legislation, whereas a rule of technology stands until and unless it is overturned by newly observed phenomena — the one is obedient to authority, the other to natural phenomena.

In the case of industrial property law, or to be more specific the law of patents, which constitute the main part of industrial property, the rules of law must be applied in two fields which are foreign to those with which the law of property and contract had traditionally been concerned. These are technology, and the intangible fruits of the brain. In the last century judges with no feeling for engineering had, when hearing patent cases, to apply the existing rules of law to steam engines, looms and electric lamps, and today they have to apply the rules developed in the patent litigation of those times to television, aircraft and polymer chemistry. Anybody familiar with patent law knows the results of this painful process of adjustment in terms of complexity, uncertainty and occasionally plain illogicality. Likewise the application of the rules of a system of law based on tangible property to intangibles, first in patent and trade-mark law, and more recently in the law of confidential information or know-how, has resulted and is resulting in similar problems.

Licensing, therefore, deals with immiscible conceptual systems which have somehow been combined in industrial property law and in the law and practise of licensing, and which involve the three types of expert: the technologist, the lawyer and the patent agent. How can the manager, for whom this book is primarily intended, best get results from this talented trio? It is the main object of this work to put the manager into a position in which he can do so.

This book is addressed to the executive of an industrial company who is charged with the responsibility for seeing a licence deal through. This person is envisaged as being a manager — perhaps a marketing, research or development manager or, less probably, a production manager — who combines the capabilities and outlook of a businessman and a technologist. He may, for example, be a technologist who has developed into a businessman, or a businessman who has acquired knowledge of the technology in which he is working.

It is in his capacity of businessman that the manager will be acting as principal in the licence negotiations and it is to businessmen that this book most frequently refers.

There are a number of books aimed at telling the businessman how to use licensing to make money or otherwise improve his company's position; these are generally written by managers or businessmen. There are also a number of books instructing the professional expert in the techniques of licence agreements; these are generally written by professional practitioners. Neither of these types of books caters for the manager in his capacity of principal in the process of setting up a licence agreement. What he needs in order to fulfil this function successfully is an understanding of the law of licensing, not in a practitioner's terms, but using his own frame of reference and his own terminology. It is this understanding that the present book will try to convey.

It would be useless to attempt an understanding of the law of licensing if one were hazy about the nature of the two essential constituents of a licence: the industrial property rights which are being licensed and the contract on which the licence is based. This is even more true if the manager in question believes he already "knows about" patents, agreements and contracts (probably a widely held belief), because nothing is less likely than that this belief is based on a true comprehension of concepts which are at least as difficult to grasp as thermodynamics or dyestuff chemistry. The first two chapters of the book are therefore intended to give an *understanding* (not a practitioner's working knowledge) of industrial property and of contract law so far as the latter is directly applicable to licensing.

Before going on to apply these concepts to actual licensing situations, the book examines in general terms how and why a licensing situation has arisen in the first place. This book does not deal with the processes of creating an innovation or of its development or with the economics of the granting or taking of a licence in respect of it; these are aspects which will in any case be in the forefront of the manager's mind. What will be lacking is the application of the manager's knowledge of research and development and its economics to the peculiar entity which is industrial property. It is hoped that an analysis of the pros and cons of a licensing policy will be helped by the present author's view of the factors involved, writing not as a technologist, economist or accountant, but as one concerned with industrial property. This view is developed in Chapter 3. This chapter is also intended to correct a bias in favour of licensing as opposed to other methods of using or acquiring technology which is very wide-spread in the literature, and sometimes amounts to little more than propaganda.

Chapter 4 assumes that a licence is to be set up and that the managers concerned know in commercial terms what they want to get out of it. On this basis Chapter 4 applies the understanding acquired from Chapters 1 and 2 to explain the make-up of the licence agreement in various typical licensing situations.

It becomes apparent in Chapter 4 that there is a hidden third party in licence agreements: the state apparatus of the country or countries concerned. In nearly every country, there is a body of law which imposes restraints on the kind of agreement which two willing parties are allowed to make with each other. The nature of these restraints, together with certain allied matters, are discussed in Chapter 5.

The theme of Chapter 4 is further developed in Chapter 6, which deals with the wording of licence agreements both in general terms and in relation to certain specific points and pitfalls which the manager needs to know if he is to deal intelligently with the professional men who will be responsible for producing the actual wording of the agreement.

Although the primary addressees of this book are managers of industrial companies, these are not the only organisations involved in licensing. Chapter 7 discusses other sources of technology and their motives and attitudes to licensing.

Just as the mingling of law and technology gives rise to the special and complex nature of licence agreements, so it gives rise to the special and complex character of the negotiating process leading up to the completion of such agreements. Chapter 8 attempts to elucidate this process.

Chapter 1

Legal basis of industrial property rights

Industrial property is a collective term for certain intangible property rights deriving from mental activity, namely the rights constituted by or inherent in patents, know-how, trade marks and registered designs. Nobody likes the term (why does it not mean the tangible assets — machinery, plant and buildings — of industry?) but it is with us as part of the generally accepted jargon and to invent a different term in this book would cause more confusion than clarity.

Industrial property is a part of "intellectual property" and the phrase was coined to denote that part of the property rights arising from "intellectual" activity which has industrial significance, as distinct from non-industrial works which are the subject of "artistic" copyright.

The borderline between works which are the subject of copyright on the one hand and industrial designs on the other has become more and more blurred, culminating with the Design Copyright Act 1968 which virtually grants copyright to any manufactured article which has been made the subject of a recognisable drawing but not of a *registered* design. (There are complications, depending on the relevant international conventions, if the drawing was made outside the UK.)

In attempting to establish property rights in the product of a man's brain, the law is faced with a dilemma. Most cerebral activity clearly cannot or should not give rise to property rights. It would be out of place in this work to enter deeply into the philosophical aspects of the matter, but the reader ought to have some idea of the problem if only to appreciate the reasons for the complexity of industrial property law. There are traditionally two kinds of intellectual property: the right which is infringed only by *copying* — that is, copyright — and the monopoly right which can be infringed either by copying or by a person arriving at the same idea independently — that is, patents, registered designs and registered trade marks. Cerebral activity which is not the subject of any of these property rights can perhaps be classified as ideas or information which have not been revealed to anybody, ideas or information which are already known to the public ("in the public domain"), and ideas (whether revealed or not) which are in some way a reflection of the outside world, such as scientific laws and discoveries.

There is, however, a way in which an important legal right can arise in respect of unrevealed information and which is based on the right of the person possessing the information to keep it to himself. This right enables the "owner" to make terms for revealing the information. In the case of information having an industrial use, these terms expressly or by implication include the extent to and circumstances in which the information may be used. Such information is called "know-how" in this book, and it will be seen that the attribution of the concepts of property rights and licensing to know-how involves some stretching of these concepts. In particular the rights arising from possession of know-how are quite different in kind from those arising from a patent. However, because the two kinds of right are inherent in one and the same physical object (a television set or a chemical plant) or process of manufacture it is not surprising that confusion can arise in dealings involving the two types of property.

Enough has been said to show that one cannot understand the licensing of industrial property without understanding the nature of the property in which one is dealing, and this chapter is aimed at achieving a general comprehension.

PATENTS

Letters patent for inventions ("patents" for short) have a long lineage in England. They were being granted by the Crown, along with other monopoly rights, in pre-Tudor times but the first legislative enactment was the Statute of Monopolies of 1628, which made all monopolies void except (under *s*6) those granted for fourteen years (now sixteen) in respect of "any manner of new manufacture."

Invention

This is still defined in the current Statute (Patents Act 1949 — referred to in this chapter as "the Act") as "any manner of new manufacture" (*s*101) but these words, archaic in themselves, derive their present meaning from case law. This evolution has inevitably been piecemeal and there is no comprehensive definition in present-day English.

As a rough-and-ready guide, one can say that an invention is a new article or substance, or a new machine, or a new method or process of carrying out an industrial operation — the word "industrial," within limits, includes agriculture and horticulture.

The patent specification

The grant of a patent can be regarded in a sense as a contract between the Crown and the patentee under which the Crown grants the patentee a sixteen-year monopoly in making or using the invention in return for a disclosure to the public of the invention and how to put it into practice. The vehicle for this disclosure is the patent specification — a document printed and published by the Patent Office as a prerequisite to every granted patent.

The claim

Besides disclosing the invention, the specification has another essential function; the definition of the area of monopoly to which the patentee claims to be entitled, this being contained in the *claim* of the specification.

It has long been recognised that to confine the patentee's monopoly exactly to his invention would stultify the whole system, since a competitor could evade the monopoly simply by making an inconsequential variation. The patentee is therefore allowed to include in his monopoly a range of constructions or processes centred on the original invention, but in return he must delineate by exact wording the total range to which he claims to be entitled. This wording is the claim of the specification.

A simple example will help to clarify this rather difficult concept. Suppose the invention is a ball-cock for a cistern. It is a mechanism which includes a float in the form of a hollow sphere. If the patent monopoly were confined to the exact mechanism as conceived by the inventor, a competitor might be able to evade it quite easily by replacing the sphere by an egg-shaped float or even perhaps a rectangular one. So the patentee does not refer in his claim to a "hollow spherical float" but to a "hollow body serving as a float" or perhaps just to a "float."

The extent to which the inventor can extrapolate from his original invention is dealt with in the Act by the provision that the claim must be "fairly based" on the matter disclosed in the specification (*s*32(1)(i)), but what is a fair basis can in the last analysis only be a subjective judgement by the tribunal or Patent Office examiner considering the matter.

The nature and function of patent claims is not made any easier by the fact that the word "invention" is used not only, as above, to mean the concrete article or process devised by the inventor but also in the quite different sense of "the invention claimed" — that is, the area of the monopoly. Although these two meanings are hallowed in the Act and by time-honoured usage generally, the word will in this book be used only in the first of the above senses, thus removing at least one semantic obstacle from the reader's path.

WHAT A PATENT IS

We can now consider what sort of thing a patent is. A simple analogy which will frequently be used in this book may be helpful. A patent can be likened to a fence erected round an area of technology and bearing the sign: "trespassers will be prosecuted." The area of technology will be recognisable as the claim discussed above, while somewhere near the middle of the area is the "invention."

By way of illustration, let us vary the theme from a ball-cock to a chemical process — say a process for making sulphuric acid by passing sulphur dioxide over a catalyst at a temperature of x $^{\circ}$C. The patentee will probably have been allowed to include in his claim a range of catalysts and a range of temperatures on either side of x. The fence delimits these ranges.

It will be observed that the fence in itself does not prevent anyone from trespassing on the forbidden area or *infringing* the patent as it is called. But once the fence is crossed the patentee has a cause of action in the High Court claiming damages and (usually much more significant) an injunction to stop the infringer from doing it again. A patent thus belongs to the species of property known in law as a chose-in-action, but it has onc peculiar feature: although it is a right granted by the Crown after due administrative process, the validity of the grant is not only open to challenge in the courts but such challenge is quite likely to succeed.

VALIDITY OF PATENTS

There is nothing in the Act which states explicitly what makes a patent valid, but s32 lists twelve grounds on which a patent may, on a petition to the court, be revoked — that is, twelve grounds of invalidity. Only the most important of these can be dealt with here. Two have already been discussed:

1 That the alleged invention is not a "manner of manufacture" as that term is currently interpreted by the courts

2 That the claim is "not fairly based" on the disclosure in the specification

Prior art

The most fundamental ground of invalidity is that, having regard to documentary or other material available to the public, or to a prior use, whether by the inventor or someone else (all of which is known collectively as *prior art*), the invention was not new. The date from which this novelty is to be reckoned is the *priority date* of the claim, the meaning of which is discussed later. Documentary material is considered to be part of the prior art if it is available as of right to an interested member of the public. Its existence and location must be ascertainable by the relevant expert, even if they are rather obscure: language is not likely to be a bar nowadays — especially if it is that of a developed country such as Japan or Russia.

A significant source of this documentary material consists of prior patent specifications which are received by the library at the Patent Office from most countries of the world. The dates from which UK and foreign specifications become effective for this purpose is discussed later.

Prior use

Prior use is a much less usual ground of lack of novelty. Its effect depends on whether or not it was "secret," this term being used to include even a normal works operation provided the public are not admitted. If the use was "secret" it is only effective if it was not "by way of reasonable trial and experiment." Commercial use will thus normally be effective.

Obviousness

The commonest ground of invalidity is probably that the invention is "obvious and does not involve any inventive step" having regard to the prior art. This means that while there is some difference between the invention and the prior art, so that it can properly be described as new, the difference is such as would have been obvious to the "man skilled in the art" such as, for instance, a "mere workshop variant."

To justify a monopoly the inventor must have taken an "inventive step." This need not be of breakthrough proportions; quite the contrary. In one case it was held that a "mere scintilla of invention" will suffice. What is certain is that there is no definition of what it consists in. As in the case of the phrase "fairly based" discussed above, it is a matter of the subjective judgement of the tribunal considering the case. It is possible by a study of the decided cases to arrive at various generalisations to assist in judging particular cases but such a study would not be appropriate here.

There is, however, one criterion which is worth discussing as it enters in one form or other into most arguments on obviousness. Let us take, as an example, the mixing of two well-known fungicides. One's first reaction is likely to be that this cannot be inventive, especially as it is generally well known to mix biocidal agents in order to enlarge their "spectrum" of activity. If, however, the inventor shows that the fungicides have a marked synergistic effect on each other, so that the mixture is more effective than the sum of the components, it is very difficult to say that it was obvious to make the mixture. The incentive was there, but nobody before the inventor thought of doing it. That the invention produces an *unexpected advantage* is thus often decisive in justifying a finding of inventiveness, although it must be emphasised that it is not an indispensable condition.

One point of detail on obviousness needs making for the sake of accuracy. Prior secret use has been included above for convenience in the term "prior art." However, this particular form of prior art cannot be deployed to found a case of obviousness, only of lack of novelty. Thus it is sufficient if the invention differs at all from the secret prior use even if the difference is an obvious one.

Inadequate or false claims

The only other grounds of invalidity we need mention (apart from "prior claiming," which is dealt with later) are that the specification does not adequately describe the nature of the invention or how to carry it out, or that the patentee failed to describe the best method known to him of carrying out the invention; and that the patent was obtained on a false suggestion or representation; for example, a false allegation of a result obtainable by the invention. Clearly any of these shortcomings would go to the root of the consideration for the grant of the monopoly.

The whole of the above discussion on validity needs qualifying in view of our determination not to use the word "invention" in a double sense. To understand the point it may be helpful to return to the analogy of a fence round an area of technology — defined with precision by the words of the patent claim — and think of the area as covering a whole range of articles or processes roughly centred on the invention. Then everything which has to be satisfied by the invention to make the patent valid must also be satisfied by the whole range of variants included in the fenced-off area. It is this which is the main factor in restraining the inventor from claiming too great an area, for the bigger the area, the more chance there is that some variant near the periphery will contravene one of the requirements for validity. In that event the whole claim is invalid — patent claims cannot be like the curate's egg; good in parts.

INFRINGEMENT OF PATENTS

A patent is infringed by anyone who makes, uses or sells an article or machine protected by the patent, or uses a process protected by the patent, or sells the direct product of such a process. To decide whether a given article is protected by the patent it is necessary to construe the definition constituted by the patent claim and determine whether the article falls within or without the definition.

British patent law is strict in holding the patentee to the words of his claim — but there are two qualifications. The first is that the *de minimis* rule (that the law takes no account of trifles) applies as always. The second is the doctrine of *equivalents* or "pith and marrow," according to which a man infringes a claim if he substitutes an element of it by an equivalent (as, for instance, a non-spherical float) so as to take the pith and marrow of the claim even if it is not within its exact wording. This doctrine grew up in the days before the patentee was required to delineate the boundary of his monopoly by an accurately drafted patent claim. Today the doctrine is given lip service but is hardly ever applied.

Court action

If the patentee wishes to go to the limit in enforcing his patent against a supposed infringer, he must issue a writ for infringement in the High Court. If he cannot tell from any product sold by the alleged infringer whether what the latter is doing infringes the patent (as in the case of a chemical process, for example) he can ask the Court for an order for discovery and inspection on the basis of a reasonable suspicion.

It is routine in an infringement action for the defendant to counterclaim for revocation of the patent on the basis that it is invalid on one or more specified grounds. The question at issue at the hearing is therefore whether any *valid* claim of the patent has been infringed.

Infringement by importing

A point which needs to be understood in the context of licensing is whether an article or substance made abroad by a process or machine which is the subject of, for example, a British patent will infringe that patent. The question arises if the British patentee did not apply for or obtain a patent for his invention in the country where manufacture has taken place, and his British patent does not contain a claim to the article or substance itself. The answer, generally speaking, is that if the article or substance is the direct product of the patented process or machine, importation counts as infringement. An exception is the USA, where importation does not amount to infringement unless the article or substance is itself claimed in the patent.

Threats

An important practical point is that unlike most other legal causes, it is actionable for the patentee or anyone else to threaten anybody with an action for infringement of a patent (*s*65). Thus an incautious word or letter may land the person uttering it in court. However, there is a complete defence if it can be proved that a valid claim was in fact being infringed. The law of threats has an inhibiting effect on the patentee who is prepared to "make an honest woman" of a suspected infringer by granting a licence. He cannot use a threat of an infringement action to bring the infringer to the negotiating table without the risk of being taken to Court for "threats."

PATENTING PROCEDURE IN THE UK

Each country has its own system of patent law and administrative procedure. In broad outline the principles set out in the preceding section, although directed primarily to the UK law, are valid for overseas countries, with a few important exceptions which will be referred to later. Administrative procedures, however, differ substantially from country to country. Those obtaining in the UK will be considered first.

Application

The first step in obtaining a patent is to file an application at the Patent Office. The applicant must be either the inventor (who cannot be a corporate person, such as a limited company) or his assignees. An assignment, for example from an employee inventor to his company, of the right to apply for a patent can be effected by signature of a *declaration of consent* to the assignee's making the application.

The application must be accompanied by a specification which may be a *provisional* or a *complete*. A provisional specification must be followed within twelve months by a complete. A complete specification must include the claim or claims which the applicant thinks he is entitled to make.

Examination

When the complete specification has been filed, the application is remitted to an Examiner who makes a search among existing UK patent specifications and informs the applicant of any which may be relevant to the novelty of the claims. He also has discretion to cite any other type of relevant document of which he may be aware.

Let us imagine that the applicant thinks he is entitled

to claim a ball-cock with any kind of float, but that (surprisingly) an elliptical float is especially advantageous in some way. The examiner cites a specification describing a ball-cock with a spherical float. This clearly destroys the novelty of the broad claim to any kind of float, but not of a claim limited to the case in which the float is elliptical. To cater for this (very common) type of situation the law provides that the applicant can make a whole series of claims directed to successively smaller fenced-off areas, each within the confines of the previous one, and that in litigation the validity and infringement of each claim is to be considered separately. In our case, claim 1 would include any kind of float and claim 2 would be restricted to an elliptical float; so that on being notified of the examiner's citation, the applicant would simply strike out claim 1 and accept the grant of a patent based on claim 2.

The examiner's remit

If, however, the examiner had missed the ball-cock specification in his search, so that a patent was granted containing claim 1 as well as claim 2, and this was challenged in litigation by a defendant who managed to discover the prior specification the examiner had missed, the court would hold claim 1 invalid but might hold claim 2 valid. If then the defendant had made a ball-cock with an elliptical float, the court would order an injunction and (subject to a defined discretion) damages for infringement of claim 2, at the same time ordering the cancellation of claim 1.

This shows that, because of a mistake, the Patent Office can grant an invalid patent, but it goes much further than that. The examiner's remit in fact only touches the fringe of the possible objections to a patent. First of all any of the world's literature which reaches the UK (and that means most of it) can be used to invalidate a patent but the examiner only searches the quite small sector represented by UK patent specifications.

Second, the Act (*ss*6, 7 and 8) explicitly confines the examiner to consideration of only a few of the possible grounds of invalidity. In particular he must consider novelty but may not consider obviousness. The reason behind this is that some of the grounds such as obviousness depend on evidence from the expert in the art, and this is not available to the examiner.

The result of these limitations on the examiner's activities is far reaching. The uninstructed layman assumes that, short of making a mistake, the Patent Office will not grant invalid patents, but this is far from being the case since some of the important grounds of invalidity will not have been considered at all.

Publication, opposition and grant

When the examiner is satisfied that the applicant has overcome all objections, he accepts the application and passes it for publication. Until this time all the papers are secret and if the application is abandoned, they will remain so. On publication, the complete specification is printed and is open for opposition (*s*14 of the Act) by any interested third party. An opponent can ask the Comptroller at the Patent Office to refuse the grant of the patent on grounds which are in a sense intermediate between those available *ex parte* to the examiner and those available in the High Court. The case is heard by the Comptroller or his delegate and there is an appeal to a Patents Appeal Tribunal.

If there is no opposition, or it is resolved in favour of the applicant, a patent is granted or "sealed" and the Letters Patent document is issued to the patentee. Within a year of the grant an interested party may apply to the Comptroller to revoke the patent (*s*33 of the Act). These proceedings are usually known as "belated opposition," as the procedure and grounds are the same as in opposition before grant.

PRIORITY DATES

It has been mentioned that to be effective against a patent claim, an item of prior art must have been dated before the priority date of the claim. If the application for a patent was filed with a complete specification in the first instance, the priority date of its claim is simply the date of the application. (This needs qualifying if the application was filed under the International Convention — see page 14.) If, however, the first specification was provisional, any of the claims of the eventual complete specification that are "fairly based" on the provisional take the priority date of the original application, while any others take the date of filing of the complete.

Prior claiming

The whole procedure, from filing the application to publication takes a considerable time — usually about two or three years — but it is only on publication that the specification counts as "prior art" against a third party's patent. What then is the position if *B* files an application after *A* has filed one in respect of the same invention but before the publication of *A*'s specification? The basic principle is easily stated but difficult to apply. It is that the Crown will not grant the same monopoly twice. Since the monopolies are defined by the respective claims, any difference in wording, even an adventitious one, between *A*'s claim and *B*'s claim makes them different, whereas as a matter of substance they may be directed to the same subject-matter. The resolution of the problem: how different must the claims be to avoid "prior claiming" of *B* by *A*? has given rise to a lot of argument and case law, some of it difficult to follow. No attempt will be made here to explain the current situation; the main point to remember is that the effect of *A*'s prior "concurrent application" on *B* is much less severe than if *A*'s specification had actually been published before *B*'s priority date. Furthermore, *A*'s claims will not count at all for prior claiming unless a patent has been sealed on his application. It should also be noted that foreign patent specifications are not prior claims and are thus only effective from their publication dates.

PATENTS ABROAD

The diversity of law and procedure and the expense of obtaining patents abroad are usually obstacles to obtaining protection in the range of countries where there is a commercial potential for an invention. There is a great deal of activity towards harmonisation and unification, notably the recently concluded but not yet ratified Patent Cooperation Treaty for unifying the initial steps and the searching procedure, the negotiations for a European Patent Office which would grant a bundle of patents effective in the various member countries according to their laws, and for a single European patent effective throughout the Common Market. However, the only important treaty at present in force to which the UK belongs is the International Convention for the Protection of Industrial Property which dates from 1883 and now includes all the industrial countries of the world.

The main provisions of the Convention are:

1 That the laws of a Convention country will be applied equally to citizens of all Convention countries
2 That if a patent application for an invention is filed in one Convention country and, within twelve months, an application for the same invention is filed in one or more other Convention countries, then such other applications will have the priority date of the first one

Hence it is very desirable for a UK applicant to file foreign applications within twelve months of his British application. If the British application was accompanied by a provisional specification, the filing of the complete specification in the UK normally coincides with the filing of foreign "Convention applications."

If an applicant (usually from abroad) files a Convention application in the UK he files a certified copy of the original foreign application and this serves to establish his priority in much the same way as a British provisional specification does for a British applicant in the UK. Thus there is no provision for filing a provisional specification with a Convention application, but only a complete.

Diversity of laws

It is not possible here to touch on the different procedures in different countries and only salient differences in substantive laws can be mentioned.

In the USA and Canada, the inventor's priority does not stem from the date of filing a patent application, but from the date he "conceived" the invention.

No country except the UK and some of the old Commonwealth countries has the provisional specification system.

The examination to which a patent application is submitted before grant varies as follows:

1 Full examination of all possible grounds of invalidity — for example, the USA, Japan, Germany and other North European countries
2 No examination at all — for example, Italy, Belgium, Spain and "Latin" countries generally, with France currently changing over to something like system 1
3 The compromise "British" system of partial examination — for example, the UK and Australia
4 Germany, Holland — and now Australia and Japan, have recently adopted the system of "deferred examination" whereby a provisional patent (not to be confused with the British provisional specification) is automatically granted for a specified period and is not examined unless the patentee or an interested party requests it within the specified period, failing which it lapses

There is a fundamental difference of approach between the UK, on the one hand, and the civil law countries and most of the rest of the world on the other (with the USA somewhere in between but nearer the UK) to the questions of definition of the monopoly area and validity. To take Germany as a typical example, there is in fact no definition of the monopoly area in the claims or the rest of the specification or in any other document. Whether any particular manufacture is within or without can only be a matter of subjective judgement after considering the specification and claims in the light of the prior art and any statements made by the patentee to the Patent Office to persuade them to grant the patent. On the other hand, the validity of a patent once issued tends to be taken for granted unless a challenger brings up fresh facts such as items of prior art which were not before the examiner. This is somewhat the reverse of the British position where the monopoly is tightly defined by the claims and the question of validity is almost completely open.

JOINT PATENTEES

A patent can be applied for and/or granted to two or more persons jointly. Assuming there are two joint or co-patentees *A* and *B*, each has the right to manufacture under the patent on his own account, without reference to the other. On the other hand neither can grant a licence to a third party (or assign the patent) without the consent of the other. It follows that in a licensing situation, the relative rights of *A* and *B* are not defined by agreeing that they shall acquire a joint patent, because they still have to negotiate the terms on which each one is permitted to grant licences. Joint patenting, as will be seen in a later chapter, is however a useful way of establishing a 50/50 interest at a stage in the relationship between *A* and *B* at which it is not possible to negotiate a full agreement on how the invention is eventually to be exploited. In a few countries, notably USA, the above does not apply, each joint patentee having the right to grant licences without reference to the other.

RENEWAL FEES

In all countries except the USA and Canada, annual renewal fees have to be paid to keep a patent in force. These vary greatly in amount and usually increase with the life of the patent. In West and, more especially, East Germany the fees are particularly onerous.

KNOW-HOW

Patents are an aspect of technological innovation. Another aspect is the body of information associated with the innovation. This can be divided into documentary information (reports, drawings and so on) and information residing in the brains and skill of the people who made the innovation.

The word "know-how" was probably meant originally to apply to the latter, but there is a tendency to use it compendiously for both kinds of information, provided they remain secret or confidential. This usage will be adopted here and know-how will be defined as all confidential (secret) technical information having industrial significance (see *Report of the Committee to Examine the Patent System and Patent Law*, Cmnd 4407, paragraph 493).

It will be noted that all innovations must include an element of know-how, but not all involve patentable inventions. Where both exist they can be regarded as two distinct types of legal rights arising from the same piece of "industrial property."

To return to the concept of a patent as a fenced-off area of technology, know-how is a map of the area giving in fine detail the location of the gold mine and instructions for overcoming the obstacles encountered in reaching it.

The attentive reader will immediately point out that the patentee is already under an obligation to describe in his patent specification the best method known to him of carrying out his invention. This is true, but the description need be only sufficient to enable an expert in the relevant technology to put it into practice, using all the knowledge generally available to such a man. There can be a big gap between a description which is regarded as sufficient to support a patent and the drawings and process details necessary to put a works manager in business.

Apart from the question of detail there is the matter of selection. It is possible for a patentee to obscure the issue by the very wealth of information he supplies. Although he must describe the best method, he does not have to identify it. For example, in a chemical case he may at the same time strengthen his legal and his commercial position by giving a wealth of experimental examples to support his patent claims while leaving it to the reader to discover which one is the commercial winner.

Know-how rights

In short, while a patentable invention represents ingenuity and insight, know-how represents hard slog, and the two give rise to different kinds of legal rights. The rights attaching to a patent have been discussed at some length; they arise from a special privilege granted by the legislature to inventors and denied to everyone else. In consequence they are carefully defined and subject to numerous reservations and safeguards, the whole amounting to a legal system of great complexity. The originator of know-how has no special position — by hypothesis it is assumed that what he has done could be imitated, given time, by any other expert of average ability. His legal position arises simply from his right to keep his mouth shut, or to open it up for a consideration. The owner *A* of the know-how can agree to disclose it to a party, *B*, and in return can exact a promise by *B* not to disclose it to anyone else. But if *B*, in breach of his contract, does disclose it to *C* then *A* cannot prevent *C* from using it or disclosing it to *D*, *E* and *F*. *A*'s only remedy is to sue *B* for breach of contract and hope to get damages commensurate with the loss incurred by the unauthorised disclosure. The court would presumably also make an appropriate order to prevent *B* from making a further disclosure, but this would be bolting the stable door after the horse had been stolen. The way in which this differs from monopoly rights attaching to a patent will be obvious.

LAW OF CONFIDENCE

Instead of making a contract with *B* under which *B* promises not to disclose know-how as part of the consideration for receiving it, *A* can rely on the law of confidence to protect his rights.

If *A* makes it clear that he is disclosing information (such as know-how) in confidence, or if the relationship between *A* and *B* and the surrounding circumstances are such that the law will infer that the disclosure was confidential, then *A* has the right to prevent *B* from further disclosure of the know-how. The use of the know-how by *B* to his own advantage is also regarded as a breach of confidence and *A* can obtain damages for such use though not necessarily an injunction. The relationship of confidence, resting as it does on a unilateral act by the owner of the know-how, is much less clearly defined in its nature and effects than the contractual relationship arising when *A* discloses the know-how by virtue of an agreement with *B*. It is the latter that is germane to the subject of licensing although those dealing with licences should understand that the unilateral right does exist and also should realise roughly of what it consists.

TRADE MARKS

It has for long been part of the common law that if *A* has a reputation in a trade name or trade mark and *B* sells his goods in association with the trade mark in such a way as to lead the public to believe that his goods emanate from *A*, then *A* has a cause of action against *B* for "passing off" his goods as *A*'s. In such an action *A* has the onus of proving both the reputation of his mark and the confusion caused by *B*'s use of it.

By the Trade Marks Act of 1875, the owner of a trade mark was given a new right: to enter his mark on a Register of Trade Marks, thereby gaining an entitlement to stop anyone else from using the mark —always assuming that the registration was valid.

An essential part of the system is that the registration must be in respect of a specified range of goods on which the owner uses or intends to use the mark, and that the registration is infringed only by use of the mark in connection with goods within this "specification of goods."

The Register

The Register of Trade Marks is kept by the Registrar who is in fact the same person as the Comptroller of Patents. As in the case of patents, an application to register a trade mark is examined to see if it complies with the requirements of the statute, currently the Trade Marks Act 1938, but in the case of trade marks the examination by and large extends to all the grounds on which a registration could be held invalid. The guiding principle is that the mark must be distinctive (in the sense that it distinguishes the owner's goods from those originating elsewhere) either inherently or because past use has in fact made it distinctive. The former is in effect a subjective judgement by the examiner or tribunal considering the matter while the latter is determined by evidence furnished by persons in the relevant trade. There are, however, two categories which are very difficult to register no matter how much distinctiveness is proved, namely words of which the ordinary significance is either a geographical name or a surname (s9*(d)* of the Act). The opposite of a distinctive mark is one which is descriptive of the goods in question. This fact, coupled with the overriding requirement (*s*11) that the mark must not be deceptive shows the narrow path which has to be trodden in many cases. For example, "Silico" for polishes might be held descriptive if they contained silicones but deceptive if they did not.

All goods are divided into thirty-four classes and separate applications must be made for goods in different classes.

Conflicting marks

A further requirement of registration (*s*12) is that the mark must not resemble too closely a mark already on the Register for the same or similar goods, unless the applicant for registration can prove "honest concurrent use" of the two marks for a period of some years. In borderline cases, the Registrar will accept the consent of the owner of the mark already on the Register as justification for allowing the marks to coexist. Whether the consent is given and if so, subject to what conditions, is a private matter between the two parties, but in practice consent is often given gratis on the assumption that the consenting party may want the same favour from the other on some future occasion.

Opposition and rectification

There is provision (*s*18) for opposition to the registration and for an action to "rectify the Register" by removing an existing registration. One ground of removal (*s*26) which will not have been considered at the registration stage is that the owner had no bona fide intention to use the mark and has not in fact used it; or that he has not used the mark for a continuous period of five years.

International

Trade marks are included in the International Convention for the Protection of Industrial Property, but the priority period is six months as opposed to twelve months in the case of patents. The trade-mark laws and practice of other countries differ from each other at least as much as they do for patents, the main point to watch being that in some countries, notably France, there is no concept of ownership of a trade mark until and unless the mark is registered, prior use being of no consequence. Hence a company which has failed to register a valuable mark in, say France, can see it lost to a third party simply by registration.

THE FUNCTION OF PATENT AGENTS

Patent agents have a function in relation to patent law and practice which is analogous to that of solicitors in relation to other branches of the law. Owing to the technological subject-matter involved, a patent agent has to have achieved at least GCE "A" level standard in a science or engineering subject, and usually has a university degree, before sitting for the qualifying examinations which the Chartered Institute of Patent Agents administers on behalf of the Department of Trade and Industry.

There is a contradiction between the difficulty of the concepts underlying the patent system and the familiarity of its main visible product — the patent specification. In many industries, patent specifications are an important if not the main source of information on recent developments and they are constantly handled by technical personnel of all grades. This means that laymen who are familiar with "patents" (as they incorrectly term patent specifications) as items of technical information are unlikely to learn the underlying concepts of the system but substitute a rough-and-ready version which usually has little relation to reality. There are, in fact, very few matters connected with patent law or practice in which it is safe to proceed without consulting a patent agent.

It is usual for patent agents to include trade marks in their practice, some training in trade marks being necessary in order to pass the patent agent's qualifying examinations. Although this is elementary compared with the training in patents, a patent agent will either have acquired a full understanding by assisting an expert or will employ a fully qualified trade-mark agent in his practice. Unlike the profession of patent agency, that of trade marks is not closed, but there is an Institute of Trade Mark Agents which administers a rigorous examination as a condition of membership. Many patent agents are members of both Institutes.

The bread-and-butter work of the patent agent is the preparation of patent applications, the main part of which is the patent specification, for filing in the UK and abroad in accordance with the various local procedures; dealing with objections raised by the various examiners and with any oppositions; securing the grant of a patent; and ensuring that renewal fees are paid on it as long as the patentee requires. To do his job properly the patent agent ought to be in *direct* touch with the inventor in any particular case.

Analogous work arises in relation to trade marks and here the agent should be in *direct* touch with the relevant marketing executive. Trade-mark matters sometimes seem simple, but in fact this is deceptive and the agent needs to have direct access to the principal actually involved just as much as he does in patent matters.

COSTS

The costs of obtaining and maintaining patents contain two components: government fees and professional charges. The Patent Office in each country has to carry out a number of clerical and technical operations on each patent application, the latter requiring skilled manpower, and the objective is to charge applicants and patentees enough to make the Patent Office self-supporting. The fee in the UK for an application with a provisional specification is still at the nominal figure of £1 but a complete specification now requires £22. The patent agent's charges depend on the nature of the job but they are not likely to be less than £40 for a provisional specification and £70 for a complete. Much higher charges may be made for lengthy or complex work.

The costs for foreign applications vary a good deal from country to country. A large fraction of the costs in foreign-language countries goes for translation. An idea of the order of magnitude of the costs and of their range can be given by quoting the estimate of the Chartered Institute of Patent Agents for an average case in India of £60 and in West Germany of £130.

It is impossible to estimate the cost of prosecuting an application since it depends on the nature of the subject-matter, the procedure of the country concerned and the objections the examiner happens to turn up. The cost can vary from a few pounds in some countries to hundreds of pounds for a difficult American case.

The annual renewal fees necessary to maintain a patent in force also vary enormously from country to country and over the life of the patent, generally increasing with its age. In the USA and Canada no renewal fees are payable and among the principal countries they are probably heaviest in West Germany, varying from about £12 to about £200 (including agents' charges) over the life of the patent. The UK is on the inexpensive side with a range of about £16 to £45.

In addition to these main costs there are one or two smaller fees to be paid at certain stages in the life of a patent application, again depending on the country concerned, but these are generally of the order of £5 or less.

Charges for trade-mark work follow a similar pattern but on a lower scale, perhaps a quarter to a half of the charge for analogous patent work. Renewal fees are only required at relatively long periods; for example, in the UK every fourteen years after an initial period of seven years.

The figures given above are quite likely to be out of date by the time this book is published. The Chartered Institute of Patent Agents publishes guides to charges for various kinds of patent and trade-mark work, which can best be obtained from your patent agent.

Chapter 2

Role of contracts in licensing

The owner of industrial property as defined in Chapter 1 has one or more of the following legal rights:

1 To prevent anyone else from entering the "technological area" defined in the owner's patent specification
2 To withhold know-how and to make its disclosure to somebody else subject to conditions about its use and further disclosure by that person
3 To prevent anyone else from using the owner's registered trade mark for the goods in respect of which it is registered

A licence under these rights is basically permission to operate in the technological area of the patent, to use the confidential information which the licensor promises to disclose, and to use the trade mark. If *A* grants a licence to *B* in return for some benefit given by *B* (known as the "consideration" for the licence) then *A* and *B* are entering into a legal relationship which is embodied in a "contract."

CONFLICT AND AGREEMENT

Perhaps one of the earliest recorded contracts was the sale of a birthright for a mess of pottage. This transaction raises a number of points which are fundamental to an understanding of contracts. First, there is the underlying relationship between the parties. It is a paradox worth dwelling on that, whereas a contract expresses an agreement between the parties, it is rooted in a conflict or divergence of interest between them. Thus, both Esau and Jacob wanted immediate access to the mess of pottage, and both wanted the birthright belonging normally to the eldest son. Their interests in relation to the subject of the contract were in conflict. However, by negotiation (at which Esau apparently was hopelessly inept) they arrived at a resolution of the conflict whereby Jacob promised to give up the pottage to Esau and Esau promised to give up his birthright to Jacob.

But there is a sense in which the resolution of the conflict underlying a contract is only transient. Once the contract has been concluded by a handshake or an exchange of signatures the parties' interests begin to diverge again — Esau would still have preferred to keep his birthright: the function of the contract is to bring into play the machinery of the law to compel him against his will to hand it over. The situation of conflict is as basic to a contract as the moment of agreement, but the habits of businessmen negotiating agreements strongly emphasise the latter and tend to conceal the very existence of the former. It is a commonplace of the negotiating table that the agreement will be worth something only as long as both parties wish it to be. If this is pressed to its logical conclusion, there would be no need for the contract: the parties would act in the same way if it did not exist. But what really underlies this attitude of the negotiators is that they would have such an aversion to going to law to enforce the contract that they would regard it as having failed in its purpose if one of them had to take this step. The contract thus serves its purpose by a kind of balance of determent which is disguised as a permanent reconciliation of the interests of the parties.

GOODWILL AND ENFORCEMENT

The attitude of the negotiators to the situation underlying the contract has significant effects on the course of the negotiations which will be discussed later. Meanwhile there is another aspect of the question of enforcement which needs to be considered. Many contracts do indeed require a measure of continuing cooperation or at least goodwill between the parties for their effective implementation. One can go further and say that all except the simplest types of contract (and very few licence agreements are that) require continuing goodwill if they are to have the beneficial effect expected by the parties.

Consider, for example, a licence under a patent. The patentee is likely to generate more information about operating the invention than is set out in the patent specification. If this information is thought to be important the parties will probably negotiate an undertaking by the patentee to impart his information to the licensee during the continuance of the agreement, but if the information is relatively unimportant the undertaking may be left unsaid, the licensee relying on the fact that the patentee can maximise his royalty returns only if he helps the licensee as far as he is able. Conversely it is normally in the licensee's interest to maximise his exploitation of the invention. Thus, while there is no express undertaking it is likely that the parties are relying on continuing goodwill to maximise the benefit of the contract.

Returning to the case where an express undertaking was given, goodwill is theoretically unnecessary because if the undertaking is broken recourse can be had to the courts to enforce it. But consider what action the courts can in fact take. They can award damages and order specific performance of the agreement. The damages may give satisfaction for past failures, but can an order by a court guarantee performance in the future?

This is the nub of the problem. A court order is in fact a very blunt instrument. You can take a horse to the water but you cannot make it drink. The commonest form of order is an injunction and this usually takes the form of forbidding somebody to do something; the law is quite capable of enforcing such a prohibition. But if the requirement is to compel someone to do something as opposed to not doing something, the position is very different. Even a simple action like paying a debt is difficult to enforce: the ultimate punishment of imprisonment is likely to make it less, not more probable. How much more so the enforcement of a complex course of action, especially if it involves collaboration with a hostile party. For instance in the example mentioned above, how could a court order be used to compel a man to divulge undocumented information the very existence of which (since it is only in his mind) cannot be determined?

It is for these reasons that undertakings other than the simplest (such as to grant a licence or to pay a royalty), particularly those involving collaboration between the parties, do in fact require continuing goodwill for their effective implementation. This goodwill is normally present when a patent licence is negotiated, but in some situations it is not. One example is where the patentee is initially unwilling to grant a licence, but is persuaded to make an offer because of a threat to apply to the Comptroller of Patents for a compulsory licence (see pages 134-5). In an actual case of this the licensee, after the lapse of a few years, complained that the licensor was being unusually uncooperative. Normally he had found that licensors were willing to answer technical questions and generally assist the licensee, but not this one. If there is no goodwill at the time of the negotiations there is little chance of its appearing later.

The fact is that the law and practice of contracts is rooted in a competitive environment. They are designed to bring together two competitive or even antagonistic parties for a specific bargain without altering the basic relationship between them. This is most obvious in the Jacob/Esau type of contract but is still true even if some kind of collaboration or partnership results. The difference is that a collaboration agreement has a deeper and more lasting effect in modifying the competitive relationship, but the relationship nevertheless continues to exist and it will usually be found that over a period of time it reasserts itself, with a consequent decay in the will to collaborate.

While it is possible to speculate that there are several forces other than the blunt instrument of the law which tend to keep the parties to their bargain, it is usually best, when the relationship reverts to the pre-contract stance, to recognise the fact and terminate the contract. For this reason it is recommended that licence agreements in which there is an important element of collaboration should have a relatively short life, at least for the collaboration provisions. This point will be returned to later.

"AGREEMENT TO AGREE"

A contract is essentially an agreement between two businessmen, either as individuals or as representatives of their respective companies. It is inevitable that when negotiating an agreement the parties try to emphasise their common interest. In simple and immediate bargains like that of Esau and Jacob, there is not much scope for this endeavour: the underlying conflict is too obvious. In contracts that require more lengthy and detailed discussion between the negotiators, there is usually one crucial point at the centre of the bargain (normally the financial consideration) on which it is hard to pretend there is a community of interest, and a number of other issues of varying degrees of controversiality. Examples of these lesser issues in patent licences are the territory covered, the duration of the agreement, whether it is to be exclusive or non-exclusive, the conditions for any exclusivity which may be granted, obligations to disclose know-how or improvements and so on. Once the royalty and any other really controversial matters (the territory is usually one of these) have been negotiated, the businessmen negotiators tend, in the interest of maintaining (or restoring) goodwill, to postpone or gloss over decisions on as many of the non-controversial or semi-controversial matters as possible.

For instance, after hard bargaining the licensor may have conceded exclusivity and the licensee may have accepted that this should be conditional on his performance under the licence, but only after an initial period has elapsed. The operation which is the subject of the licence has, by hypothesis, at least some degree of novelty and this, coupled with all the usual uncertainties of a manufacturing and marketing operation, makes it extremely difficult to forecast what would be a reasonable measure of satisfactory performance (such as an annual minimum royalty) and the number of years after which the criterion should begin to be operative. What the businessmen would like to say in the contract is, "the parties will consult together after (say) three years and agree an annual minimum royalty."

Another more acute example of the same frame of mind is the situation in which a prospective licensee promises to do some evaluation work on the patentee's process or product in return for "an option to take a licence." It is at this point that the area of conflict shifts from that of businessman *A* versus businessman *B* to a sort of three-cornered fight between businessmen (*A* + *B*) versus lawyer *A* versus lawyer *B*. The lawyers object to what they call "an agreement to agree" and the businessmen rather uncomprehendingly tell each other that the lawyers will not let them indulge in what seems to them a perfectly reasonable expression of the goodwill which has brought the parties together.

In fact the lawyers are right. They are remembering the underlying situation of conflict which is paradoxically the raison d'être of the contract. If the relevant interests of the parties were the same, there would be no need for the contract. This, for example, is the situation with a company and its wholly-owned subsidiary. If the parent owns a patent, it does not need to negotiate a licence with the subsidiary to work it, except perhaps for formal or tax reasons. If, on the other hand, the parties are independent, an agreement to agree is in fact meaningless because they cannot be made to agree. Thus, in the case of the "option" the only obligation on the patentee is to make the other party an offer. If the terms of the offer are prohibitive (for example, a very large royalty) the other party can do nothing about them and finds that he has in fact done the evaluation work for nothing.

In the case of the exclusive licence clause, the only real obligation on the parties is to consult after the three years. It would depend on the exact wording of the clause whether failure to agree would leave the licensee with his exclusivity or relieve the licensor of it, but the scope for conflict and misunderstanding is obvious.

What is the remedy? The businessmen sometimes say to the lawyers: "You are objecting to our reasonable 'agreement to agree,' so what do you suggest we put in its place?" The answer of course is that the lawyers are not objecting, they are merely pointing out that the phraseology conceals a failure to make a bargain and if the parties want a bargain they have to make it. It may be conceded, for instance, that it is in the nature of the evaluation agreement that the terms of the eventual licence cannot be negotiated before the evaluation has been done, in which case the patentee must agree to give some other consideration to the evaluating company. The parties may agree to share the risk of their not agreeing on the terms of a licence by each paying half the evaluation costs, or the patentee may agree to pay all the costs in return for having free use of the evaluation results if no licence can later be negotiated.

In the case of the exclusive licence example, the situation is rather different, since the agreement to agree is limited to a part of a larger agreement. Probably there is no alternative, if the parties really cannot agree on the minimum royalty figure, to making the licence exclusive for the three years only "unless the parties can agree on a figure at the end of the three years." This leads to another matter. Businessmen at this point would always insert wording to the effect of the passage in quotation marks, whereas the lawyer would tend to omit it. A clearer case of this difference of view is where the parties negotiate a royalty but realise that market conditions may later dictate that it is inappropriate. They may propose to say that if the royalty turns out to be greater than the market will bear, the parties will meet to agree a lower figure.

Neither of the above cases is a mere agreement to agree; a firm agreement has been made, but the parties are saying that it can later be altered if they agree to do so. Businessmen set great store by this sort of wording, but lawyers always resist it because they point out rightly that any contract can be altered at any time by agreement, and to say so is superfluous. This difference is, however, more a matter of style than of substance but it can introduce a note of controversy between the client who feels that the wording helps the negotiations and the lawyer who prefers not to be associated with loose, untidy draftsmanship.

To sum up this section, the businessman negotiator, in emphasising the positive aspect of the negotiations, often fails to allow in the wording of the contract for the likelihood that the initial goodwill will decay. The best corrective for this is to ask in relation to any matter where agreement between the parties will be required: "What happens if they fail to agree?" These matters are well understood by the lawyers, who are likely to tell their clients in effect to go away and negotiate a real, not a pretending, bargain. While the lawyers are undoubtedly right here, it will be seen later that there is another area of misunderstanding at which the honours are perhaps more evenly divided.

TYPES OF INDUSTRIAL PROPERTY CONTRACT

So far in this chapter the discussion has been applicable in principle to any type of contract. The remainder will deal more specifically with contracts concerned with the licensing of industrial property.

Patent licences

A licence under a patent is, as noted above, in its simplest form the granting of permission to the licensee to enter the patentee's "fenced-off" technological area. The patentee can agree to withhold this permission from anyone else and to stay out himself, in which case the licence is "exclusive." Alternatively he may make no such promise ("non-exclusive" licence) or adopt an intermediate course of agreeing to grant no further licence but retaining freedom to enter the territory himself ("sole" licence) or to grant only a limited number of further licences. The licence is granted for some consideration and in principle that is all the licence contract need consist of. In practice, however, there are usually other terms, dictated by the particular nature of patents for inventions.

The terms in their totality can be exactly as the parties manage to negotiate, subject to certain statutory limitations. These arise from the fact that monopolies are prima facie contrary to public policy, that it is possible by the terms of a licence effectively to extend the scope or duration of a patent monopoly beyond that which is inherent in the patent grant and that the legislature will not tolerate such extensions. The statutory limitations vary from country to country and will be dealt with more fully below, but it will be noted here that in this country they are of secondary importance, in the USA they are fundamental and in most other countries they lie somewhere between these extremes.

Know-how licences

If a person is in possession of know-how, which has been defined as confidential technical information having industrial significance, he is free to disclose it or keep it to himself. He is thus in a position to make terms for disclosing his know-how to another party. This disclosure by itself is of no value; only by using the know-how does it become valuable. The use can vary from technical or economic evaluation, through providing a starting point for research or development, to full-scale use for production. Contracts which relate to only the first two of these uses are usually referred to as secrecy agreements rather than licences, but the connection is close and secrecy agreements will be dealt with below.

Licences to use know-how for commercial production are first cousins to patent licences and are often part of the same contract. This is because the object of a patent licence is to enable *B* to make commercial use of an innovation by *A* in which know-how rights also reside. Although a patentable invention and a corpus of know-how may both reside in the same technological innovation, the nature of the legal rights arising from what are virtually two sides of the same coin are radically different. (That they are different can be emphasised by recalling that patent rights depend on publication while know-how rights depend on secrecy.) This somewhat paradoxical situation often leads to confusion.

RELATIONSHIP BETWEEN PATENT AND KNOW-HOW LICENCES

Suppose *B* hears that a process developed by *A* for purifying a certain chemical by solvent extraction is available for licensing. The crux of the process is the use of a particular solvent X_1 which is sufficiently ingenious to amount to a patentable invention. *A* has obtained a patent covering the use of solvents of the class *X* and has fulfilled his obligation of disclosure by describing some laboratory experiments of the process using half-a-dozen solvents *X* one of which is X_1. Over the last couple of years, *A* has developed the process to the commercial scale and has in his possession know-how consisting of the identification of X_1 as the commercially interesting solvent, flow sheets of a plant including a suitable solvent recovery section, detailed drawings of the plant including specifications of specialist components, and process specifications giving such details as the temperature and time of the extraction stage and the temperature of the solvent removal stage. *B* is anxious to start building the plant but believes the operation cannot be profitable unless he gets exclusivity.

Licensing terms are discussed in Chapters 4 and 6. For the moment attention will be focused on disentangling the patent licence and the know-how licence from the package deal which *A* is offering *B*. Assuming that *B* is technically/commercially oriented and has little feeling for the legal niceties of the situation, his efforts will be concentrated on laying his hands on the know-how. As part of the routine he refers the matter to his legal/patent adviser *Q*, but tells him not to worry too much about the patent — it is the know-how that matters. *Q* accordingly does not undertake an investigation of the validity of the patent. An exclusive licence agreement is concluded and *B* goes into production in the time it takes to build the plant from *A*'s drawings and get it on stream.

When the plant has been operating successfully for a few months *B*'s main competitor *C* gets to hear of it, learns that *B* has an exclusive licence under *A*'s patent and asks his legal/patent adviser *R* to see if he can break the patent. *R* finds a prior publication which invalidates the patent (see page 6) and *C* sets to work to design and construct plant for carrying out the process. While it took *A* two years to do this, *C* can take some short cuts. In the intervening time, Professor *G* has published certain research relating to the physical chemistry of the solvent which gives *C* clues about the process details. Information has leaked out regarding *B*'s plant and process — for example, there are rumours in the trade regarding the type of centrifuge and distillation column, both of which *B* bought out. Finally one of *B*'s staff leaves and takes a job with *C* and certain hints are passed, which *B* has no hope of detecting, let alone proving. In the result, *C*'s plant goes on stream only one year after *B*'s, and *B* finds that his lead time is quite inadequate to secure a reasonable return on his investment.

B immediately instructs his lawyer *Q* to advise on what action could be taken to get *C* out of the business or at least make him pay tribute. *Q* tells him that the only action that can be taken is for infringement of the patent (which action *B* could take as exclusive licensee), but that, having carried out a search, he has found a prior publication (the same one that *C* discovered) which invalidates the patent. Although the contract with *A* contains a provision that *B* need no longer pay royalties in the event of unlicensed infringement, he is nevertheless powerless to prevent the competition either from *C* or anyone else who may jump on the bandwagon.

RELATIVE VALUES OF PATENT AND KNOW-HOW

It is commonplace to hear that it is the know-how that is valuable, not the patent, and that the point of the patent is to provide a peg on which to hang the know-how agreement. There is a conceptual difficulty underlying this attitude. To return to the example, what *B* was buying was a process and, because the deal was exclusive, he was assured that *A* would not sell the process to anyone else. In consideration, *B* undertook to pay an agreed price in terms of royalties, a downpayment or whatever else was negotiated. It was not in *B*'s mind, however, that in negotiating the price he was in fact paying for two disparate values, both inherent in one and the same technological innovation: the value of the patent licence and the value of the know-how licence. To *B*, the real value he was getting was the know-how and the assurance that *A* would not sell it to anyone else. The patent licence was some kind of extraneous abstraction in which *B* was not interested.

It is not normally necessary to make a separate commercial valuation of the patent and know-how components of the contract (although a valuation may be necessary or desirable for tax purposes), but the result of such a valuation would be somewhere between two extremes:

1 The patent is of little value because of a low presumption of validity or a narrow scope of the claims, and the know-how comprises a great deal of very valuable information over and above that found in the patent specification
2 The patent is presumed valid and of wide scope, and there is little know-how over and above the information in the patent specification

There is no necessary relationship between the information in the patent specification and the value of the patent licence. The only effect of this information on the comparative valuation is to reduce the relative value of the know-how to the extent that it has been published in the patent specification.

It will have become apparent (to return again to the example) that in respect of the patent, *B* was paying for a position of continuing exclusivity (which was illusory as it turned out). But there is another value arising from the patent which is even harder for *B* to take into account, and which applies whether the licence is exclusive or non-exclusive. This is the promise by the patentee not to sue the licensee for infringement of the patent or, in other words, the patentee's permission to the licensee to enter the "fenced-off area," which is inherent in the patent licence. This immunity is just as necessary to enable the licensee to go into business as the other elements of *A*'s package. To recapitulate these, there are:

1 The know-how licence
2 The promise by *A* not to grant such a licence to anyone else
3 The immunity from a patent infringement action
4 The exclusivity of this immunity which effectively transfers the patent monopoly right from *A* to *B*

A given licence contract can include any or all of these although of course one cannot have 2 without 1, or 4 without 3.

SECRECY AGREEMENTS

Before two parties *A* and *B* embark on licence negotiations they may decide that *B* should be given a significant amount of information relating to the subject of the licence, in order to enable him to evaluate the technical or commercial aspects, or the patent aspect if the relevant patents have not yet been granted. While it may be possible in theory to rely on a relationship of confidence to protect the disclosure of information, the parties usually prefer to take advantage of the greater certainty and definition of a contractual relationship by concluding a secrecy agreement.

In principle such an agreement between *A* and *B* should include two undertakings by *B*:

1 To keep the know-how secret
2 To use it only for a specified purpose

In the case of a pre-negotiation evaluation the purpose is clear and can readily be defined. There are, however, many situations in which *A* is willing to disclose know-how but has considerable difficulty in defining his reasons for doing so. This may sound improbable, but an example will illustrate the point.

It is quite common, at least in some industries, for company *A* to receive a representative of company *B* for a variety of more or less well-defined reasons. It may be that *B* wishes to acquire some information of an ancillary character such as marketing potential in a given area or concerning the supply of some raw material, and *A* is willing to oblige in the hope that *B* will do him a similar favour on another occasion. More frequently an element of collaboration is involved. *A* and *B* may be contemplating common action against *C*, or a possible merger, or defensive action in the face of government disapproval or requirements in respect of a product both companies are making.

At one time *A* would simply have relied on the relation of confidence inherent in the situation, but unfortunate occurrences, particularly in relation to ex-employees and to unsolicited disclosures by outside inventors, have made companies more secrecy-minded and it is not uncommon, for instance, for the representative of *B* to be presented with a secrecy agreement to sign before he is allowed into *A*'s works. Such an agreement is necessarily in standard form and therefore is unlikely to specify the purpose for which *B* is to be allowed to use the secret information or know-how he may acquire. The agreement may thus say boldly that the know-how must not be used by *B*, which is absurd since *B* has not travelled all the way to *A*'s works for nothing; or it may be silent on the subject of use and thus provide less of a safeguard than the law of confidence.

But whether or not a secrecy agreement specifies the use to which the know-how may be put, there is one fundamental problem to which there appears to be no answer. Once *B* has received a piece of information, it is part of his stock of knowledge and cannot be disregarded in *B*'s future cerebral activities. The result of this is either that *A*'s information may enter into *B*'s research activities in a way *A* never intended, or that *B*, in leaning over backwards to avoid this situation, is inhibited from undertaking a justifiable research project.

COLLABORATION AGREEMENTS

The transfer of know-how in one direction, from *A* to *B*, has been discussed. Frequently, however, the parties decide to exchange information. This is usually an essential part of a collaboration agreement. The collaboration may relate to research, development or marketing, though the last is liable to lead to difficulties under restrictive practices and similar legislation. Even R & D collaboration is suspect under US anti-trust law. (These matters are discussed in more detail in Chapter 5.)

We have indicated the inherent unsuitability of the contractual relationship for regulating a collaboration. An undertaking by the parties to collaborate in, for example, a research project may be little more than a pious hope unless it also involves definite obligations in relation to payment of research costs or activities by research staff. It may well be, therefore, that the real heart of a collaboration agreement is in fact the provision for exchange of know-how. Such an agreement is really two secrecy agreements welded into one document, and the reciprocal provisions have the effect of cancelling out the underlying difficulty of the permitted use of the know-how by the recipient.

An R & D collaboration agreement is incomplete unless it includes provision for the exploitation of any resulting industrial property rights. This will be discussed later, but it should be noted here that while (as indicated above) collaboration agreements should generally be of short duration, it does not follow that any licences granted under the agreement, particularly licences granted to third parties, should also be short-lived.

TRADE-MARK LICENCES

A valid trade-mark registration gives the proprietor a monopoly in the use of the mark in connection with the goods for which it is registered. So far as contract law is concerned it is open to the proprietor to allow someone else to use the mark in connection with those goods in return for a consideration, and the bargain can be embodied in a contract between the parties. The resulting licence to use the trade mark can, as in the case of a patent licence, be exclusive, non-exclusive, sole or partially exclusive. Effectively the licensor is transferring to the licensee the goodwill, or a share of the goodwill, associated with the mark.

There is, however, a legal restriction at the heart of trade-mark licensing. The duties of the Registrar of Trade Marks include preventing any use of the Register or the registration system in such a way as to cause any deception of the purchasing public. The basic purpose of a trade mark from the proprietor's point of view is to inform the public of the origin of the goods on which the mark is used. From the point of view of the public it is a guarantee that the goods will be of a similar quality to those purchased before under the same mark. This latter expectation is due not to any obligation on the proprietor to abide by any standard of quality — there is no such obligation — but to the inherent interest of the proprietor in retaining the goodwill of his customers. However, the law has taken it on itself to back up this inherent self-interest with a certain measure of compulsion. Originally the law did not permit the licensing of trade marks since the public would not know whether they were buying from the original source or a different one. The sanction was the loss of any proprietary rights in the mark.

At the present time practically all countries permit the licensing of trade marks, but stipulate that the proprietor must be able to control the quality of goods sold under the licensed mark. Any contract for the licensing of a trade mark should therefore include provisions having this effect. The law is far from pursuing the matter to its logical conclusion, since there is no provision for compelling the proprietor to make use of the control provisions he has written into the contract. Thus, so far as avoiding deception is concerned, reliance has still to be placed on the proprietor's own self-interest.

FORM AND LANGUAGE: LAYMAN VERSUS LAWYER

A contract is concluded when one party has made an offer and the other has accepted it. Contrary to what is often supposed, a binding contract does not have to have any special form. Businessmen often seem to think that a contract written in ordinary English in the form of a letter is somehow less significant or less binding than one written in "legal language" on foolscap or double-brief paper, and especially if it is executed under seal with ribboned pages and some of the traditional law stationers' embellishments. In fact (and leaving aside oral contracts) any piece of writing expressing an agreement, whether on letter paper or the back of an envelope, provided it is signed by both the parties concerned, is just as binding as the most formal of legal documents.

This statement is not quite complete without referring to the necessity for "consideration." This simply means that in order to set up a contract, the party who is offered something must give, or promise to give, something in return. It is up to the parties to negotiate what the consideration is to amount to, but consideration there must be. So far as licensing is concerned this point is of practical importance only if the parties wish to conceal the consideration by keeping it out of the document which grants the licence. In that event the licensor can simply execute what is in effect a deed of gift to the licensee and provided this is executed under seal it is enforceable by the licensee. However, the licensor might have difficulty in holding the licensee to whatever bargain they secretly made. It should be noted that such a deed differs from a contract based on "consideration" in that its form is essential to its validity. The necessity for consideration does not apply to all countries. In the USA the matter is governed by state law but, in general, consideration is necessary. The special form of a deed of gift is probably peculiar to the UK and closely related countries like Australia. In the USA the point would be met by providing a nominal consideration such as the proverbial one dollar.

"LEGAL LANGUAGE"

The object of this chapter is to give businessmen an understanding of what licence contracts and negotiations leading up to them are all about. It might seem that in this broad context the question of language would be out of place as a mere detail. In fact it is a vital part of the ever-present tension between the lawyer and the layman hinted at earlier in this chapter. It would be surprising if, in a traditionalist discipline such as the law, forms of language had not evolved which could be described, according to taste, as correct modes of expression which have stood the test of time, or archaic jargon used to bolster up a mystique.

Controversy apart however, the language of the contract ought to serve the sole purpose of recording clearly, unambiguously and with as much precision as possible the matters which have actually been agreed between the parties. Unfortunately, this statement is itself ambiguous, since what is clear language to the lawyer is often obscure to the layman, while what is sufficiently precise to the layman is often ambiguous to the lawyer. Precisely the same dilemma arises in the drafting of patent claims. There are judicial pronouncements to the effect that claims for engineering inventions should be in language which is readily understood by the engineer. By "engineer" the judges have meant, without fully realising it, their own judicial idea of what an engineer would think. The fact is that the function of a patent claim is to define the patentee's monopoly and in any dispute this definition is construed not by engineers but by lawyers, so woe betide the patent draftsman who takes the judge's pronouncement literally.

THE BUSINESSMAN'S DEAL

To return to contract language, it is on the one hand desirable that the wording should conform with the lawyer's requirements and on the other that the businessmen should thoroughly understand what they are signing. A fairly common pattern of events is for two businessmen who want to make a deal, and to make it unencumbered with legal advisers and their complexities, to write down their version of what they have agreed and then ask the lawyer to "put that in legal language." The chances are that this is an impossible task because the lawyer finds the "instructions" incomplete in one or more of the following ways.

Agreement to agree The businessmen have not really made a bargain at all, but have merely told each other their hopes and intentions. For instance they may "agree" that they will collaborate on a research project and each party will have an option on an exclusive licence under patents obtained by the other. As indicated earlier, such an "option" is meaningless unless the terms of the licence have been agreed. As for the collaboration, it is likely (again, see above) that this amounts to no more than an agreement to exchange confidential information, but if the lawyer converted the businessmen's full-scale "collaboration agreement" into nothing more than an undertaking to exchange information he would get short shrift.

Inadequate definition The businessmen have not troubled to give accurate definitions of some of the concepts involved. These can vary from the fundamental to the detailed. An example of the first is likely (indeed almost certain) to be one of the most important parts of the contract — its technological field. For instance the parties agree to communicate know-how "in the field of chromium and related compounds." The parties have probably not worked out exactly what they mean by the quoted wording and would need to be cross-examined to get at the answer. This is where the lawyer is in a difficulty, because his training does not usually include any scientific background and he will have no feeling for the matters he is trying to elicit from his client. This part of the work can be better done by a patent agent, who has a foot in both camps. For example, he may discover that what the businessmen really want to agree about is compounds of metals in Group VI of the Periodic Table — something the lawyer may never have heard of.

As an example of a detailed point inadequately defined, consider: "A royalty of 5 per cent on the selling price of —." Does this mean the gross selling price or the price net of various deductions, and if so what deductions?

Impossible promises The businessmen may have made promises they are not in a position to fulfil. A not uncommon example of this occurs when company *A* has invented a process such as the one referred to before for purifying a chemical, and wishes to make an agreement with company *B* under which *B* will develop equipment for carrying out the process. *A* promises *B* that, in return for the development effort, *B* will have the exclusive right to sell the equipment to users licensed by *A*. However, it is unlawful for *A* to make it a condition of a licence that the licensee shall purchase from *B*, and the agreement between *A* and *B* cannot be implemented (see pages 123-4).

Contingencies There are various possible problems which the businessmen will probably have forgotten. For example: What is to happen under a patent licence if an unlicensed third party infringes the patent? Shall the licensee go on paying royalty in competition with a manufacturer who is operating royalty-free?

It is this kind of deficiency in the businessman's informal agreement which is liable to lead to most difficulty in the client/lawyer relationship. With regard to the other three types of shortcoming, the client may start off by being impatient with the lawyer but can soon be made to see that his "instructions" do in fact need supplementing. On the matter of unlicensed infringement, for example, the client is apt to say: "This is a lawyer's matter — settle it with the other chap's lawyer." The lawyer replies that there are various ways of dealing with this particular problem, and he cannot settle the matter until he knows which methods his client wants. As will be seen in Chapter 8, there is a case for the negotiating company to appoint a person to act as a coordinator of licence negotiations who understands both the legal and technical/commercial points of view and has executive power to settle those points whose practical importance is not commensurate with their legal complexity.

COMPROMISE

Having clarified the businessmen's intentions to his satisfaction, the lawyer now has to draft an appropriate contract. Here again the problem of language intrudes. One might think that there is only one form of words to express a given meaning. In practice language is not quite as accurate as that. Thus, if a lawyer and a businessman equally well trained in the English language were asked to express a given concept, they would probably produce different wording. It is a moot point which should be used in the contract. In the last resort the intention will be judged by lawyers but the last resort seldom arrives and in the meantime it is advantageous if the two men who are to implement the agreement really understand what it means. Probably a compromise approach is best. Let the lawyer sacrifice any unnecessary archaisms such as the avoidance of punctuation, and any special forms of a purely stylistic significance; and let the businessman be ready to tighten up his phraseology wherever the lawyer feels this to be really necessary in the interests of precision (looked at from the lawyer's point of view).

An advantage of the approach just described is that it takes one some of the way to a style suitable for the non-common-law countries. Licensing of industrial property often involves other countries and it will be found that the sort of phraseology lawyers prefer in common-law countries (chiefly England and the USA) is not at all suitable for, say, continental Europe.

To sum up this discussion, the businessman's idea of a contract is likely to be very incomplete, not only because the legal way of thinking is unfamiliar to him, but also because he has a strong predisposition to emphasise his common interest with his negotiating partner and push into the background the underlying conflict of interest of which the contract will only represent a partial and temporary resolution. This, of course, represents his predominant feeling at the time the parties are negotiating but experience shows that it is also usually the most successful negotiating stance. At all events the net result is a tendency to gloss over or defer as many controversial points as possible and hope that the lawyers will settle the rest.

Chapter 3

Decisions to take or grant a licence

A person who manufactures goods has to sell them in order to get a return; a prospective purchaser usually has the option of buying or not buying them. A person who has generated an item of industrial property (patent, know-how and/or trade mark) is generally in a different position, since he is not obliged to "sell" (grant a licence) in order to get a return; he has the option of retaining his industrial property rights and working them himself for his own benefit. This chapter is concerned with the considerations which arise in deciding whether to grant or take a licence. (The verb "to license" will be used to mean only "to *grant* a licence." It is becoming common to use the verb also to mean "to *take* a licence," but this usage is thought to be inappropriate and confusing and will not as a rule be used here. An exception to the rule will be the use of the term "licensing-in" to denote the activity of taking licences, as opposed to "licensing-out.") This subject can be discussed in relation to several parameters, such as the nature of the underlying relationship between the parties, the degree of importance of the item of industrial property and the nature of the property in relation to the type of user (large or small companies; manufacturer or customer).

THE DECISION TO LICENSE

The decision whether to grant or take a licence is a management decision. Fundamentally it ought to be based on an estimate of the relative profitability of the alternative of keeping the rights to oneself in the case of licensing-out, or the relative cost of generating the technology oneself in the case of licensing-in. This may sound too obvious to need stating; but as will be seen, the fact that the decision is about an unfamiliar and abstract type of property (the "chose-in-action" referred to in Chapter 1) can confuse the basically simple issue.

THE "LICENSING EQUATIONS"

It is clear that the considerations are radically different as between granting and taking a licence. In the first, the question is whether the monopoly rights in an innovation generated by a manufacturer can be used more profitably in the manufacture and sale of goods, or by charging a consideration for allowing a measure of competition or giving someone else the monopoly.

In the second, it is whether it is more profitable for an organisation to buy an innovation from outside or to generate the corresponding technology itself.

These two equations involve, as it were, a licensing term and a non-licensing term. In the licensing-out case the "non-licensing term" is computed by the familiar exercise of assessing the profitability of a particular line of manufacture in relation to the estimated presence or absence of competition — an exercise with which it would not be appropriate to deal in this book.

In the licensing-in case, the "non-licensing term" of the equation involves the process of generating industrial property rights — a process which is in every way relevant to the subject.

It is necessary, in following the discussion in this chapter, to be clear about the terms of these "licensing equations", which are summarised in Figures 3:1 and 3:2.

IN FAVOUR OF TAKING A LICENCE		AGAINST TAKING A LICENCE	
1	Cost of own R & D = cost of experimentation to achieve objective X probability of failure	1	Cost of R & D to adapt and operate licensed technology
2	Length of time required for 1	2	Length of time required for 1 from beginning of negotiations
3		3	Benefit of strengthening own research effort
4	Strong patent situation	4	Weak patent situation
		5	Consideration to be paid for licence

FIGURE 3:1 TERMS OF THE LICENSING EQUATION: LICENSING-IN

IN FAVOUR OF LICENSING		AGAINST LICENSING	
1	Consideration to be obtained for licence	1a	Loss of monopoly position (non-exclusive licence)
		1b	Exclusion from operation (exclusive licence)
2	Cross-fertilisation of ideas	2a	Promotion
		2b	Legal and patent fees
		2c	Marshalling know-how
		2d	Guarantees and technical service
		2e	Securing a patent position

FIGURE 3:2 TERMS OF THE LICENSING EQUATION: LICENSING-OUT

It will be noted that the terms of the licence (other than the financial consideration) do not figure in either of these lists. This is because the main decision tends to be on whether to take or grant a licence at all — and in this chapter it will, by and large, be assumed that terms are not a deciding factor. Clearly terms such as exclusivity, territory and so on can be vital. They may in certain cases tip the scales for or against a deal at some point sooner or later in the decision-making process. Consideration, however, of the significance and import of the licence terms belongs more properly to the parts of the book dealing with licence agreements as such.

A factor in both licensing-in and licensing-out decisions is the size and sophistication of the company. In the case of licensing-in there is a reasonably clear inverse correlation between size and sophistication on the one hand and readiness to take licences on the other. The "not-invented-here" syndrome tends to be more pronounced the larger the research and development organisation the inventor is trying to penetrate. In the case of licensing-out there are factors which work in opposite directions. Thus a small company which hits on an innovation will have more difficulty than a big one in satisfying the market; it will, therefore, be more anxious to maximise its returns by licensing. On the other hand the small company will be less well-equipped for the tasks which are actually involved in carrying out a successful licensing-out policy and which are discussed below under costs of the licensing operation. These deficiencies can to some extent be made good by hiring outside brokering or professional expertise.

LICENSING-IN

It is part of our industrial civilisation that manufacturing organisations are open, or potentially open, to competition. This may arise within a country, across national boundaries or across ideological boundaries. It follows that there is a constant urge to innovate: to make a new product, improve an existing product or cut costs. How does this innovation take place? As a rough-and-ready guide we can say that innovation is generated by the following functions of a manufacturing company: patentable inventions by the research function, know-how by the development or design function and trade marks by the marketing function. In considering whether to look for innovations to buy in from outside or to spend the money in generating the innovation from one's own resources, it is the cost and potential (allowing for the likelihood of success) of research which are the most difficult to estimate. It is relatively easy to estimate the costs of developing a given process, or designing a given plant or machine, or promoting a product under a new trade mark. The objective and the means required to achieve it are, by and large, known.

Research is quite a different matter, since the outcome is, by hypothesis, unknown — a situation alluded to in many an epigram fixed to the walls of research managers' offices. Moreover, industrial research can vary over a wide range in its degree of fundamentality.

Nevertheless, industrial research must (or should) be directed towards a clearly defined objective of the company. In the context of industrial property licensing it is likely that the relevant objective will be concerned with the development of the company's products or processes. Such objectives will be referred to as "development objectives."

Thus in considering whether to take a licence or do one's own research (and it is only this aspect of the large subject of research management that is relevant here), the first requirement must be to formulate the development objectives at which one is aiming. The formulation of development objectives, which may be the function of a company planning and development department (to be distinguished from the process and plant development referred to above), involves long-term financial, market research and inter-company political considerations and is again a subject on its own which cannot be dealt with in this book.

THE DEVELOPMENT OBJECTIVE

The starting point must be a defined development objective. To show more clearly what is meant some examples are listed of recognisable types of development objective:

1 A glass company seeks a method of making the equivalent of plate glass for the cost of sheet glass
2 An electronic company wishes to exploit the properties of solid state materials
3 A chemical company discovers a deposit of anhydrite under its premises and seeks a process for converting this raw material into cement and sulphuric acid

4 A fibre company seeks a new fibre with specified properties
5 A chemical company is looking for new uses for one of its products

The first task (and this may be related to the search for the objective itself) is to study what is already available or appears, from the literature and private sources, to be likely to be available in the near future. If nothing is found that interests the company, then it must decide to do its own research, drop the objective, or put it in cold storage till something turns up.

Assuming there is a product or process available which the company believes it could use (either in its present form or after development within the company) and it finds that this is available for licensing on stated terms, the sort of considerations which might arise in deciding whether to pursue the matter are as follows.

Research costs In order to make a valid comparison between taking and not taking a licence, the best attempt possible must be made to quantify the money which would be required for a research project culminating in the achievement of the objective within the company. Research workers sometimes chafe at this kind of management control on the basis that it fails to take account of the unpredictable result which may produce a "bonanza" at relatively small cost. The correct way of dealing with this is to assess the cost of the research effort as the cost of the experimentation needed to produce the bonanza result assuming success at the first attempt, and multiply this cost by the probability of failure estimated as best one can.

However it is estimated, whether logically or as a hunch or by a mixture of the two, the research cost for arriving at the hoped-for innovation must be compared with the licensing terms.

In considering research costs, it should also be borne in mind that the need for research and development will not be obviated altogether by taking a licence. This is because there will normally have to be some redesigning and adaptation of the technology to the licensee's particular environment and also some technical service and development work to support the new business.

The time factor As with all management decisions the aim should be to quantify the variables in money terms, leaving, as far as this can be done, as little as possible to guesswork, however inspired this may be. One such variable in the present context which may indeed be decisive in many cases is the elapsed time of going into production following one's own research on the one hand and of operating under licence on the other. These times should be estimated and, if at all possible, a money value should be put on them.

The value of research in its own right The third factor is even more difficult to assess and quantify and may perhaps be a company objective in itself: the desirability of strengthening the company's research effort as an investment in its own right, on the basis that much of the value of the facilities set up for the particular project would remain valuable for future projects, as well as strengthening the general technical capability of the company.

The patent position Finally an assessment of the prospective licensor's monopoly position must be made. If there is a published patent, the research project may resolve itself into finding a way round the patent claims. It can be stated as a general proposition that no patent can cover every solution to a problem. Moreover, as has been seen in Chapter 1, the greater the breadth of the patent in relation to the fundamentality of the inventive step on which it is based, the greater the likelihood that it is invalid.

It is possible in principle to estimate in terms of time and money the effort which would be required to by-pass the patent, either by devising an alternative solution outside its scope and/or by building up a convincing case against its validity. This estimate must be included in the overall cost of relying on one's own research.

EXAMPLES OF DEVELOPMENT OBJECTIVES

These considerations are all highly subjective and uncertain. It may help if a brief glance is taken at the development objective situations set out on page 51 from the point of view of a company wishing to enter the field. The assumption is, of course, made that the company which developed the technology is willing to license it on terms reflecting the situation as outlined in each case. The point of view of the potential licensor is considered under "licensing-out" on page 56.

New process for plate glass In the glass situation the governing factor will probably be time. In order to remain viable in the market, the company will need to adopt the new process without delay. The patent position would not have to be very strong to convince the company not to waste the time necessary to by-pass it.

Solid state electronics While it is quite likely that a "new" process for making an old product like glass could have been anticipated in its broadest terms by some crackpot publication of long ago, in the case of a new science such as solid-state electronics this is most improbable. The situation, therefore, lends itself to a fundamental patent position. The time factor may be less important to the potential licensee than the desirability of gaining a deep insight into solid-state phenomena, and the company may therefore decide not to take a licence if the estimated cost of by-passing the relevant patents is not prohibitive.

Conversion of available raw material There is an implication in the anhydrite situation that the chemistry of the process is known and there would be little advantage in setting up research to investigate it. The main requirement may be know-how which it would pay to buy in.

New fibre In the fibre case, any patent is likely to be based on the fibre chemistry rather than its properties, so the company may decide to look for an alternative fibre with similar properties in preference to taking a licence.

New use for a product This is a situation in which research by the company is indicated. If, as is supposed here, another company has invented one or more new uses for the product in question, it is likely to be a competitor whose main motive is to secure a market advantage in the sale of the product. To compensate for licensing a competitor, a high fee would be required. It is true that the inherent legal difficulties in exploiting use patents have the effect of restricting the severity of the terms that can be asked but this is likely to be decisive only in the USA.

PRACTICAL CONSIDERATIONS

The above discussion may seem a little unrealistic in that it presupposes that the company considering taking a licence is in a position to contemplate taking on a research project; in other words that it already has a research base and can estimate, as it were, the marginal cost of adding a new project. The discussion also presupposes a "market" in innovations such that, when a development objective is formulated, the company can go shopping in this market. In fact neither of these presuppositions may be true. The company may have no or only a minimal research base. Starting a research project would then mean a substantial change of attitude and managerial habits, all of which costs time and money.

Likewise it would be unusual if there were one or more innovations on offer to match a given objective, even if "on offer" includes prospects sought out by the prospective licensee. It is perhaps more likely that the process is reversed, with the company learning of an innovation which could be the subject of a licence and then working out whether this prospect should be matched by a development objective. Again, the company without a substantial research base may make a business of actively seeking licences as its main means of innovating. The point to notice is that even, or perhaps especially, in these situations a correct decision can be made only if it is based on a development objective properly arrived at, and on the best estimate of the various factors indicated above for and against achieving the objective by carrying out research internally instead of taking the prospective licence.

LICENSING-OUT

The position of the company considering whether to grant a licence is rather different. Licensable industrial property rights are usually (bearing in mind that it is only manufacturing companies that are being considered) a by-product of the originating company's main activity. This is not always so, particularly when a company discovers a new use for one of its products or invents a machine for converting one of its products into a finished article. The exploitation of any resulting industrial property rights is then in the mainstream of the company's activity, since it is an integral part of marketing the product in question.

In the more general case, the licensable rights reside in a company product or a process for making it rather than (or in addition to) rights in the use of the product by the customer. In such a case any licence granted represents a loss of existing or potential markets, while an exclusive licence effectively puts the licensor out of business in the territory concerned.

Reverting to the equation mentioned above (the price of the loss versus the income from the licence), the question of assessing the profitability of a particular manufacture in the presence or absence of competition is (as already indicated) not one for discussion here. On the other hand the factors in a licence agreement that can affect the degree of competition introduced by the licence (in this case non-exclusive — the question does not arise with an exclusive licence) are relevant. They will be mentioned briefly at this point, but considered more fully along with other licence terms in Chapter 4.

FACTORS AFFECTING COMPETITION

The most obvious factor affecting competition is the territory of the licence. For example, a British company may decide to license a Japanese company to make a certain product in Japan. The question is: In which other countries where the licensee has a good marketing position should he be allowed to sell the product? Suppose the British company has an established marketing position in New Zealand and is already selling the product there; it has a rather shaky marketing position in Australia which it might be able to expand by selling the new product, provided a good deal of promotional effort is made. It has no hope of marketing in any of the east and south-east Asian countries in which the Japanese company is interested: if this is true, the licensor loses virtually nothing by licensing the Japanese company to sell the product in the Asian countries. In New Zealand it is likely to be more profitable for the British company to withhold a licence. The reason for this is that royalties for a licence can represent only a fraction of the total profit on the sale of the product. It will, therefore, be profitable to give up a share of the market to the Japanese competitor only if there are special reasons why it could be unprofitable for the British company to cover the whole market in New Zealand. It is Australia which, in this example, gives rise to the most difficult decision. The pros and cons of on the one hand materially increasing the sales effort in Australia, with the side-advantage of putting the whole marketing operation of the company on a sounder basis, and on the other of collecting royalties for virtually no effort are probably fairly evenly balanced.

The assessment of the relative merits of marketing or licensing in a given territory will depend to some extent on any governmental regulations regarding these activities. Businessmen will in general be familiar with restraints on marketing such as import duties. Restraints on licensing, or more accurately on realising an income from licensing, also exist in some countries, notably Japan and the developing countries such as India. These will be referred to in Chapter 5.

Apart from territorial provisions, the royalty payable by the licensee, and, indeed, any burden placed on him when operating under the licence, itself has some effect in reducing his competitiveness as against the licensor. The relative positions of the parties would also be affected if one of them invented an improvement in the product which was being licensed. Many licence agreements provide for the automatic grant of licences under any improvements, either by the original licensor to the licensee, or by the original licensee to the licensor or (more usually) in both directions.

COST OF THE LICENSING OPERATION

Consideration has been given to the effect of certain licence provisions on the degree of competition introduced by the licence. Another term on this side of the equation — that is, against licensing — is the cost of the licensing operation itself. This may be made up of the following components:

Legal and patent costs The legal costs are not likely to be significant compared with the other components. As regards patent costs, these can be considerable but in the present context only costs in countries in which patents are obtained solely for the purpose of the licence need be taken into account. Those for countries in which the licensor would patent whether or not he intended to grant a licence are not relevant to the cost of the licensing operation.

Promotion It is hardly necessary to point nowadays to the untruth of Emerson's remark that if a man invents a better mousetrap the world will beat a path to his door. If a man makes a conventional sort of mousetrap he should be able to market it by ordinary promotional methods, but if the mousetrap he is trying to sell is new and unorthodox then he has to add to this the effort required to convince the public that the device works at all, let alone that it works better than the old ones. In other words if a company wishes to license an innovation it will in general have to find a prospective licensee and then convince him that he needs the licence. The cost of this promotional effort should be estimated as accurately as possible and put in the scales on the debit side of the licensing operation.

Marshalling the know-how The industrial property rights which are being considered for licensing may include or consist entirely of know-how. This will normally have been generated by the company as part of its own research and development effort, and the licensable rights residing in it are therefore available as a by-product. The special cost of licensing these rights consists in assembling the information, writing descriptive material and making drawings, and producing the whole as an attractive package. Of course it may be possible to make a direct charge for these items, even including a profit, but the cost still belongs on the debit side of the balance.

Guarantees and technical service These are often provided for in licence agreements, but even if they are not, the licensor may find it difficult to turn a deaf ear to a licensee who finds himself in difficulties in operating the licensed technology. In the nature of the case, the cost of such services cannot be assessed in advance, but some provision should be made in weighing up the to-license/not-to-license balance.

Securing a patent position There is another rather more elusive element in the cost of licensing which is related to the setting up of a patent position. It belongs in a sense to the patent costs referred to above but is different in kind from the professional and government fees which make up those costs. While it has been assumed so far that the licensable rights have arisen as a by-product of the company's main-stream activities, this may be only partly true. This is because a sound patent position is more important for successful licensing than it is for protecting the company's own manufacturing operation. For the latter, it is merely one of many factors needed to secure the company's competitive position, but for licensing it is central. Just as know-how must be marshalled and put together in an attractive package if it is to be saleable, so a patent position must be convincing, not only to the patentee, but also to the prospective licensee and his advisers.

HOW THE PATENTING OPERATION CAN GO WRONG

It will be remembered from Chapter 1 that a successful

patent covers not only the actual invention made by the patentee but also as wide an area surrounding it as can validly be claimed. Two necessary conditions for this are a sound and broad experimental base, and sound professional handling of whatever material is available, both of which cost money. An example of the sort of thing that can go wrong will make the point clear.

A company making a chemical *X* wished to find new uses for it. On the basis of an intelligent study of the literature, the research manager concluded that one of the physical-chemical properties *P* of the chemical would make it suitable for an operation *O* carried out by his company and also by a large number of companies who were potential purchasers of chemical *X*.

Experiments apparently confirmed that *X* produced excellent results when used for *O* in an environment suitable for exploiting the property *P*. A patent specification was written up based on this experimental work and the property *P*, and patent applications were filed in a number of countries.

Later it was observed by the patentee that *X* could also be used in an environment outside the range suitable for exploiting the physical-chemical property *P* and therefore outside the range claimed in the patent specification. By this time a policy of exploiting the invention by widespread licensing of customers had been decided on and the company realised to its consternation that its patent position did not hold water and would soon be found unconvincing by prospective licensees.

The company, therefore, put in hand a thorough programme of research into understanding how *X* really operated in the operation *O*. It was found that a property unrelated to *P* and requiring a different environment was responsible and that it was purely coincidental that the original range of environmental conditions suitable for the two different properties happened to overlap near their edges.

Unfortunately, the extension of the range beyond that originally disclosed did not amount to a patentable variant of the original patent applications, and it was therefore too late to repair the damage.

Thus, while the original experiment provided the company with a new and useful way of carrying out operation *O* and the original patent claims provided a useful deterrent against others from imitating the process, these claims were not adequate to provide a sound basis for a licensing policy. If the company had realised the position and had embarked on a full-scale research project at the outset, it could have secured sound patent cover to support the licensing policy.

Allocating the cost

In the last example, the initial incomplete research was associated with the patentee's own manufacturing operation, and the later research (if it had been carried out early enough to contribute to the patent) would have assisted the licensing operation. Should the costs be allocated accordingly? At first sight the answer seems to be yes, but this could be an oversimplification, since the sounder patent position secured by the extra research would also be effective in strengthening the patentee's own competitive position. Perhaps the correct allocation would be an equal share to manufacturing and to each licence.

INCOME FROM LICENSING

Assessing the income from a licence is no less uncertain and subjective than estimating the costs of the licensing operation. In fact the correct rate of royalty (or equivalent consideration) is what the traffic will bear, and it may be necessary to enter into discussion with a prospective licensee before anything like a reliable estimate can be made. In other words some steps towards promotion of the industrial property must be taken before deciding on whether to adopt a licensing policy.

EXAMPLES OF LICENSING-OUT

With all these difficulties in the way of a logical approach, it may be useful to discuss from the point of view of the company considering granting a licence the five situations referred to in the consideration of licensing-in policy.

New process for plate glass It would probably be unrealistic to aim at supplying the whole plate-glass market even in a single country. A licensing policy is therefore indicated. In view of the breakthrough proportions of the innovation, high returns from licences can be expected.

Solid-state electronics This project creates a new market rather than supplying a cheaper version of a conventional product. The innovating company may, therefore, reasonably hope to supply the entire market for an initial period. After this, pressures for local manufacture may become strong enough to warrant going over to a licensing policy.

Conversion of available raw material Here the process is likely to be worth more to the prospective licensee, who happens to have virtually free access to the raw material, than to the owner of the process. Licensing is therefore indicated.

New fibre As in the solid-state electronics case, the product is a new one, and the innovator can reasonably hope to supply the market himself. A non-licensing policy is likely to be more profitable than licensing.

New use for a product Clearly the innovator will wish to license his customers but withhold licences from competitors and those users who purchase the product from competitors. The constraints on this policy are legal rather than economic, and will be considered more fully in Chapter 5. Similar remarks apply to the case in which the supplier of a raw material, for example glass, invents a machine for converting the material into a finished article — for example, bottles.

THE LICENSING PARTNER

The foregoing discussion assumes that licensing policy is independent of the identity of the prospective licensee or licensor. This assumption is in general not warranted. Factors which will weigh in the balance, in addition to all those mentioned above, in a particular potential licensing situation will include the view one party takes of the integrity, reliability and capability of the other; its commercial policies and ambitions; and above all its existing and potential affiliations.

Another general factor which is impossible to quantify is the cross-fertilisation of ideas which may result from a licensing arrangement involving a technological exchange.

THE BIAS IN FAVOUR OF LICENSING-OUT

All other things being equal, there is a general weight of opinion in favour of licensing-out but against licensing-in. Probably this is mainly because it is the person who has benefited humanity by making the innovation that is in a position to grant licences. The other party is the passive recipient. Of course if there were no people prepared to take licences, none could be granted, so the general bias tends to cancel itself out except where the prospective licensee is less susceptible to public opinion than the prospective licensor. There is, however, another bias of less significance, but nevertheless noticeable, which works in the direction of licensing in general; it makes the licensor more ready to grant and the licensee more ready to take a licence. This bias originates from the zeal of the various people involved in the actual work of setting up licensing situations and licence agreements. It is thought to be only fair to the reader to remind him that the present author is one of these people.

Chapter 4

Licensing situations

The reader, armed with basic information on, and some understanding of, industrial property and the contractual relationship, and aware of the considerations entering into decisions on whether to embark on a licence deal, will now wish to learn in more detail about the nature of licence agreements and how they are set up.

The matters which need to be dealt with in a contract depend on its subject-matter. For example a lease of accommodation should provide for the rent, the term of the lease, responsibility for repairs, right of entry and so on; a contract for the sale of goods involves the price, date and place of delivery, shipping, insurance and similar items.

MATTERS ARISING IN LICENCES

In the same way licences under industrial property rights involve their own particular set of terms. In attempting to list these it must be remembered that each licence agreement is the progeny of two people (or teams) each of whom can exercise his ingenuity in thinking of ways to exploit an inherently complex and uncertain situation. An exhaustive list of the possibilities obviously cannot be drawn up but the following should provide an adequate basis at least for the initial consideration of a deal. On the other hand not all the listed terms will appear in every agreement; on the contrary many agreements will involve only a few of the possibilities. In addition to straight licence agreements, the policy followed in previous chapters will be adhered to of including agreements for collaboration in research or development which are ancillary to or closely connected with the exploitation and therefore the licensing of industrial property.

1 *Types of agreement*
Licence agreements
Collaboration agreements*
Preliminary or assessment agreements
Option agreements
Hiring agreements

2 *Industrial property involved*
Patent(s)
Patent application(s)*
Know-how*

3 *Nature of the licence*
Extent to which monopoly rights are ceded; exclusive, sole, partially exclusive and non-exclusive licences
Operational rights granted: manufacture, use, sale
Territorial extent of each of these
Technological extent: wider or narrower than, or coextensive with, the "fenced-off area" of the patent
Right to grant sub-licences

4 *Consideration for the licence*
Royalty based on extent of use of licensed rights
Minimum payments (usually annual)
Downpayment
Grant of licence from licensor to licensee (cross-licensing)

5 *Collateral provisions**
Technological field for collateral provisions
Transmission of know-how
Provision of technical assistance

Secrecy of know-how
Rights under new technology (improvements)
Quality control (especially for trade-mark licences)
Price control
Supply of unpatented materials or parts
Performance guarantees: by licensor
by licensee
Restriction of right to export

6 *Duration and termination*
Normal life of agreement: as a whole; particular parts
Premature termination
Rights after expiry or termination

7 *Servicing of the contract and the licensed industrial property*
Mode and time of payments to licensor
Records and inspection of books
Establishment and maintenance of the industrial property: prosecution of patent and trade-mark applications and payment of renewal fees
Covenant not to dispute validity of the licensed patents etc*
Infringement of licensed patents etc by third party
Most-favoured licensee clause
Infringement of a third party's patent by licensee
Mode of communicating (serving notice)
Applicable law (which country?)
Arbitration

* The subjects marked with an asterisk are danger areas under US anti-trust law. The main thrust of this elaborate system of restraints is two-pronged. First, any agreement tending to reduce competition between the parties is contrary to the basic concept of anti-trust. Hence any collaboration agreement is automatically suspect. Second, the use of the patent monopoly to restrain or control any activity other than actual infringement of the patent (that is, trespassing on the "fenced-off area") is regarded as a misuse of the patent which is contrary to anti-trust law. This strikes at most if not all of the collateral provisions that may be introduced into a licence agreement. It will be seen in

Chapter 5 that the ambit of anti-trust law is being expanded by a continuous process of interaction between the administrative and judicial branches of the US government, and this makes it difficult to give a definitive statement of the position even at a given moment of time. Thus, for example, a recent decision has brought into question, it is believed for the first time, the whole question of the legality of know-how agreements.

Most other countries also impose some restraints on the content of licence agreements, but none which approach the US anti-trust law in severity. Perhaps the maximum freedom among the main countries exists in the UK. This makes it convenient to discuss agreements in the context of UK law and later to explain in the light of this discussion restraints which may be imposed in other countries.

Industrial property contracts represent agreements reached between two parties to express a particular relationship between them. There is an infinite variety of such relationships, but the subject can be organised by recognising certain types of pattern. The basic theme, which also recurs in more complex situations, is the simple patent, trade mark or know-how licence.

SIMPLE PATENT LICENCE

The type of situation to consider here is that in which a company, pursuing a certain line of activity, finds an obstacle in its path. This obstacle is in the shape of a patent which the company believes to be valid or at least is not prepared to challenge. The assumption made here is that all that the company wants is freedom to go on its way. This is a licence in its simplest form; a promise by the patentee not to sue the licensee for infringement of the patent. To put it positively, it is a non-exclusive licence to make, use and/or sell within the fenced-off area of the patent.

As has already been seen, this area may represent, according to the nature of the innovation in question, a new article of manufacture (such as a ball-point pen), a new machine, a new industrial or agricultural process or a new product (such as a chemical). These are defined in the "claims" of the patent (see Chapter 1), and a given patent may contain claims to more than one of these types of innovation — for example, to a new product and a process for making it. Now a patent claim is infringed by making, using and/or selling (as appropriate) anything within the area defined by the wording of the claim. In addition it is generally held that a claim to a process or a machine is infringed by selling the direct product of that process or machine. Usually a British licensee will be given the right to do any and all of these things under the British patent — that is, in the UK — but this is a matter for negotiation and there could be special circumstances in which he would have obtained more restricted rights.

One such possibility that comes to mind is where the patent claims a chemical which is useful for flameproofing plastics. A company wants a licence to make the chemical and also to compound it in the plastics it makes. It would further like to extend the licence to enable it to sell the chemical in the open market. The licensor, however, is willing to grant a licence only to make the chemical and use it (that is, to compound it with the plastic), but not to sell it, and this could be the basis of the deal. The converse is, of course, also possible (though less usual in practice), where the patentee is willing to let the licensee make and sell the chemical, but not to use it, thus reserving for himself exploitation in the field of flameproofing of plastics.

Details of phraseology which may be used for this and other matters discussed in this chapter are given in Chapter 6.

Patent not yet granted

Since it usually takes years for a patent to be granted, it may happen that negotiations for a licence agreement take place while the patent application is still pending. As there is at that stage no monopoly right, no licence can be granted; but it is quite in order for the parties to agree on the terms of a licence. The further step can then be taken of an agreement by the licensor to grant, and the licensee to accept, a licence on these terms when and if the patent is granted. It is usual, furthermore, to agree that the terms of the eventual licence shall be effective, so far as they are applicable, while the patent application is still pending. Thus, for example, the royalty is payable as if the patent had been granted. The consideration for such payment is the security the licensee has of continued freedom to operate after the patent is granted — clearly a matter of vital importance if investment in plant and promotion is to be made.

Corresponding foreign patents

A licence under the UK patent gives no rights under any overseas patent for the same invention, but it is usual to negotiate any licences required under overseas patents at the same time as the British patent and include them in the same agreement. Perhaps the commonest provision is to give the licensee a licence to make *and* sell under the UK patent but only to sell under the overseas patents (that is, export to the countries concerned).

If (as is usual) the UK licence includes the right to sell, no further licence is needed to enable the licensee to export to countries abroad where there are no corresponding patents. On the other hand it is possible for the parties to agree that there shall be *no* export to one or more such countries, but this is a collateral matter, not part of the licence as such.

ROYALTY

In the simple case under review here the consideration for the licence is likely to be a royalty commensurate with the extent of use of the licensed rights. There are two ways of expressing this royalty: as a percentage of the sales value of products made and sold under the licence or as a sum of money for a defined number of articles or quantity of product made and sold. The royalty is, of course, the crucial matter in most licence negotiations and it is also likely to be the one on which the least amount of factual information is available to the negotiators. The importance and uncertainty of the royalty aspect of the agreement result in negotiators giving undue prominence to the terms in which the royalty is expressed. There are two aspects to this: first, whether the royalty should be expressed as a percentage or as a sum per quantity sold; second, the product on which the royalty should be based.

Clearly the logical way of charging royalty is as a percentage of sales value, since this allows for the changing value of money and any other change in the price of the product. However, for reasons which are not altogether clear but are obviously subjective in character, businessmen sometimes prefer to express the royalty as "£*x* per ton" or "£*y* per 100 pens." At the date of the agreement the actual sum payable would be indistinguishable from one expressed as "*p* per cent of the sales value of the product," but after a lapse of time the two amounts will diverge. It is, therefore, usual to make provision at least for the effect of the changing value of money if the first method is used, by agreeing that *x* or *y* shall vary in proportion to some figure, such as the cost-of-living index or some published raw-material cost, which expresses the changing value of the currency.

The question of the product on which royalty should be based could arise, for example, in the case of a patent for a new chemical whose use is as an additive for petrol, or a patent for a machine for making stockings. At first sight the royalty could be charged as a percentage of the sales value of the chemical or of the sales value of the machines. However, the chemical may be used only to the extent of a few parts per 100 000 of the petrol, and only a handful of the stocking machines may be sold. The real benefit of the invention lies in the ultimate product: the petrol or the stockings. Thus a reasonable return for the invention might be represented by 0.1 per cent of the sales value of the petrol or stockings, whereas if the percentage were based on the actual subject of the patent, the royalty would have to be 500 or 1000 per cent. There is, however, an unwritten convention that a royalty of 10 per cent is very high and one of 1 per cent is rather low, so the negotiator who asks for 500 or 1000 per cent is going to be laughed at while the one who asks for 0.1 per cent will be well received even if the actual money involved is exactly the same.

Diminishing royalty rate

Negotiators tend to take into account not only the percentage of sales which is to be paid but also the total sum of money on the basis of estimated sales. If the estimated sum per year looks fairly small, a higher percentage will often be conceded by the licensee than if it looks large. This (again rather subjective) approach sometimes leads to a sliding scale of royalties whereby the royalty rate decreases in steps as the sales per year increase.

DURATION AND TERMINATION

The duration of the licence is normally for the life of the licensed patent. It is in any event useless to provide for a longer duration, since under *s*58 of the Patents Act either party has a statutory right to terminate the agreement on three months' notice after the patent has expired.

There is no particular reason, in this type of licence (which is, of course, non-exclusive), for the licensor to have the right to terminate the agreement prematurely; the licensor can grant further licences if he wishes to and it would be unreasonable for him to be able to shut down the licensee's operation; although an exception to this is the commonly provided right to terminate if the licensee is in breach of his obligations, such as by failure to pay royalties.

The question whether the licensee wants to be able to terminate prematurely is bound up with other provisions which will be dealt with below.

COVENANT NOT TO DISPUTE VALIDITY

It is obviously of concern to the prospective licensee to know whether the patent in question is valid or not. This, however, is not a matter on which he can expect any help from the patentee. The doctrine of *caveat emptor* applies in a way familiar to those with experience, for example, of buying or selling a house. There is, furthermore, an implication that if a person takes a licence under a patent he is accepting that the patent is valid. This is reflected in the common law doctrine that in the absence of any express provision in the agreement, the licensee is "estopped" from disputing validity. Presumably, however, this is so only as long as the agreement is in force, and the licensee would therefore like to have the right to terminate the agreement whenever he wants to. In that case, if he discovered some reason why the patent was invalid, he could terminate the agreement and continue to operate royalty-free in the knowledge that the patentee could not successfully challenge him.

For safety's sake a provision equivalent to the common law's estoppel is often written in the agreement as an explicit undertaking by the licensee not to dispute validity. Sometimes the licensor succeeds in having the undertaking written in such a way that it has no time-limit. In that event the licensee would not be interested in having the right to terminate the agreement even if he found the patent to be invalid since he would not be able to defend himself by pleading such invalidity. There is, however, some doubt whether the courts would uphold a covenant not to dispute validity after termination of the licence.

It is not suggested that the matters discussed in this section are of great practical importance; indeed some of the points border on the far fetched. Nevertheless it is desirable for businessmen to understand the types of point that may crop up in an agreement and the rationale behind them.

INFRINGEMENT OF LICENSED PATENTS

This matter is related to those discussed in both the previous and the next section. If a third party ignores the patent and operates without paying anything to the patentee, it is hardly fair for the licensee to have to continue paying royalties. The licensee will therefore wish to include in the agreement some remedial provision. This can take one of the following forms:

1 An undertaking by the licensor to sue any infringing party. Either the licensor would succeed in such an action, thus stopping the infringement, or he would fail, in which case the licensee would know that what the alleged infringer was doing did not in fact come within the patent and therefore did not rank for royalty payment under the licence agreement; and/or that the court would revoke the patent,

thus enabling the licensee to terminate the licence under *s*58 of the Act.

2 Suspension of royalty payments until and unless the licensor had "abated" the infringement by granting the infringer a licence or by suing him for infringement.

3 The parties agree to consult and, if the licensor does not wish to sue for infringement but the licensee is willing to do so, the licensor will lend his name to the licensee to enable the latter to take action at his own expense.

These matters are somewhat complex; various changes can be rung on these provisions and more blood may be spilt on them than is commensurate with their practical importance. The only certain thing is that although 1 is the simplest way of dealing with the matter on paper, no licensor in his senses is willing to enter into an unconditional undertaking to sue for infringement of a patent.

MOST-FAVOURED LICENSEE CLAUSE

This is often called a "most-favoured nation clause" by analogy with custom-duty treaties between nations. It is an undertaking given to licensee *B* by licensor *A* not to grant a licence to any other person *C* on terms more favourable to *C* than *B*'s terms are to *B*. Again, there can be considerable complications in the details of such a clause (see Chapter 6). In any case it is a difficult one for the licensor to resist.

INFRINGEMENT OF THIRD PARTY'S PATENT

This is another matter whose importance is usually to be measured by the amount of confusion it can cause rather than by its positive significance. In the first place it is often not apparent to the businessman that the fact that operation under patent *Y* infringes another patent *X* does not in general reflect on the validity of patent *Y*.

This can readily be seen by reference to the fence analogy. *A* has discovered a technological area for which he is granted patent *X*. Later, *B* discovers a particularly valuable area within the boundaries of patent *X*. This entitles *B* to the grant of patent *Y*. If, now, *C* seeks a licence from *B* under *Y* he in fact needs a licence both from *A* (because he first has to cross fence *X*) and from *B* (to cross fence *Y*). It is, therefore, not unusual for *C* to request from *B* an assurance that in operating the licence he will not infringe any third party's patent. Such a request is in the author's opinion misconceived, since the matter is outside the control, and usually outside the knowledge, of *B*. The most that *C* can reasonably expect is an assurance from *B* that he is not aware at the date of the agreement of any third-party patent which *B* will infringe.

But what if there is in fact such a patent? The answer must surely be that the royalty rate demanded by *B* must take account of the fact that *C* has also to make his peace with *A*, so that the final product will have to bear two royalty payments. If the existence of patent *X* is not known to either party at the date of the agreement but *C* fears that there may be such a patent, the agreement could provide for renegotiation of the royalty if either party became aware of the hypothetical third-party patent.

This concludes the terms which, generally speaking, are applicable to the simple patent licence, and which are likely to be significant to business negotiators. The remaining terms of the basic licence tend to be non-controversial and are discussed, along with the finer detail of those dealt with above, in Chapter 6.

SIMPLE TRADE-MARK LICENCE

In theory it is possible for the proprietor of a trade mark to grant a non-exclusive licence to another party to use it in return for a consideration which could be a royalty on sales of goods under the trade mark.

The only term of such a licence calling for special mention is that which provides for inspection and quality control. It was explained in Chapter 5 that, in order to reduce the possibility of deception of the public by the use of a trade mark by two different companies, any licence under a registered trade mark has to permit the licensor to inspect goods destined for sale under the trade mark and to terminate the licence if the goods do not achieve a standard laid down by the licensor.

But is the concept of a simple trade-mark licence, analogous to the simple patent licence, really valid? If a company *A* is considering using a trade mark which is the same as, or confusingly similar to, another company *B*'s trade mark, it would be no solution for either party for *B* to license *A*, since it would be in neither's interest to use the same mark. It could happen that *A* stumbles on a mark of *B*'s which *B* is not interested in using, but then the likely solution is for *B* to assign the mark outright to *A* for a down payment, thus avoiding the complications of a licence which would be of no benefit to either party.

SIMPLE KNOW-HOW LICENCE

If a company is aware that another company operates a successful process which it would like to imitate, it can negotiate a licence for the know-how. Although we may call the deal a "licence" it in fact consists in the transmission of certain confidential information (referred to in this book as "know-how") from the "licensor" to the "licensee". This transmission is made subject to an agreement, an essential part of which is implied or express permission for the recipient to use the know-how for his own commercial benefit. Whatever may be the abstract legal theory about the existence or absence of property rights in unpatented know-how, the right of the person possessing it to keep it to himself if he wants, or to make conditions for disclosing it, in fact makes it a saleable asset. It is the permission to use the know-how for the "licensee's" own commercial benefit that makes the transaction akin to a licence under a patent. Such a deal can be distinguished, for example, from the case in which the recipient agrees to use the know-how only for carrying out work under contract to the donor, or as a basis for research and development.

One of the important consequences of the true nature of the know-how licence will emerge in Chapter 5 where the difficulties which have recently arisen under US anti-trust law in connection with this kind of deal are discussed.

Definition of the know-how

In the simple case being considered, the know-how is in effect a pin-point on the technological map rather than an area. It can therefore be defined as the know-how in the licensor's possession relating to the manufacture of, say, polythene or, to be even more precise, the know-how relating to the process in use by the licensor for manufacturing polythene.

Agreements relating to know-how over a technological area are possible, but they tend to belong to more complex types of situation and will be considered later.

Technical assistance

Transmission of know-how, to be complete, should include the sending to the licensee's works of the employee or employees who have, in their heads or as part of their skill, relevant information not previously recorded in writing or drawing. It is advisable, however, to include the provision of such assistance in the contract if only because it involves agreement on various ancillary matters such as the number of people involved, their length of stay in the licensee's works and their remuneration while they are there.

Secrecy

It is in practice an essential part of the agreement that the licensee undertakes not to disclose such information as is confidential to any third party.

Performance guarantees

It is also of the essence of this type of agreement that the know-how, when put into effect by the licensee, shall work. That is what the licensee is paying for. It is therefore usual to include performance guarantees by the licensor. The sanction for failure to meet the guarantees can range from ceasing to make any further payments to the licensor, through refunding to the licensee payments already made, to penalty payments by the licensor. Alternatively the licensor could supply technical assistance. The nature of the sanction will normally be bound up with the time-scale laid down for fulfilment of the guarantees; the longer the time, the higher the penalty.

Consideration
In the type of agreement under review, the licensor's obligation is discharged when he has transmitted the defined know-how and fulfilled any performance guarantees. Payment of a specified sum of money by the licensee may therefore be appropriate, made either as a single down payment or spread over a number of years. There is the possibility of royalty payments, but this raises a difficulty fundamental to the nature of know-how as distinct from patents. It is possible for know-how to leak out, or to be developed independently by a third party, and the licensor can do nothing to stop its use in competition with the licensee. In such a situation continued payment of royalties would hardly be equitable. This point is developed below.

Duration and termination
It is a characteristic of know-how that any property rights in it are dependent on its non-availability to the public. It is true that if *A* communicates information to *B* under conditions of confidentiality the courts may hold *B* liable to *A* for use of the information even if, unbeknown to the parties, it was available to the public at large; but this is a matter between *A* and *B*. There is nothing *A* can do against persons who learnt the information independently. It follows that the value to *B* of know-how transmitted by *A* rapidly dwindles if and when the information ceases to be secret. Since this is generally outside the control of *A* or *B* the question of the duration of the agreement gives rise to some theoretical difficulty. In practice, however, difficulty is likely to arise only if the consideration for the licence takes the form of royalty on production. This may occur if the licensee is unwilling to agree to a specified sum of money great enough to satisfy the licensor that he is getting an adequate return.

If royalties on production are payable, the duration of the agreement is crucial. The licensor will try to make it as long as possible, and the licensee will at least try to include a provision for termination if the know-how ceases to be secret otherwise than through the licensee's own fault. Another possibility is to provide for termination if there is substantial manufacture by an unlicensed third party using the know-how. This, however, would be very difficult to prove.

If the agreement does not provide for royalty payments, the only other continuing obligation is that of the licensee to keep the information secret. It is common form to provide that the licensee is released from this if the information becomes known otherwise than from the licensee, but even so it is usual to place a maximum term of years on the licensee's obligation to maintain secrecy, if only for practical reasons.

Taking all these things into account, it is not unusual to fix a term of ten or perhaps fifteen years for the agreement, with the licensee being meanwhile relieved of his obligations as indicated above if the know-how ceases to be secret. Naturally if the consideration for the licence is a fixed payment spread over a number of years, the payments ought to be completed whatever happens, and the licensor should see that there is no loophole in the agreement on that score.

Right to use know-how after termination

A vital question too often overlooked in the courtship days of negotiation is the right of the licensee to go on using the know-how after expiry or termination of the agreement. If the agreement is silent on this point, the licensee has, *prima facie*, no right to go on using the know-how after the agreement which *effectively* gave him that right has ended. The attentive reader will note the two qualifications in the last sentence. There is indeed some doubt about the origin of the licensee's right to use the know-how and this doubt reflects on the statement that the licensee has no right to use the know-how after expiry or termination of the agreement. (The doubt on whether the licensee would be prevented from using the know-how after termination is, of course, much greater if the know-how has become public than if it is still secret.) The salient point about this is that it is a matter of prime importance to the licensee to be able to continue to use the know-how after termination of the agreement for two reasons: first it is likely to be impossible to disentangle his own know-how from that received years ago from the licensor and, second, the know-how may be a part of the licensee's commercial operation or even built into his plant, so that stoppage of the right to use it could mean a shut-down of the operation. In a matter as vital as this surely the licensee should resolve any doubt when the agreement is negotiated, and insist on an explicit provision that he *can* continue to use the know-how after termination. The licensor is unlikely to demur at that stage of the proceedings whatever his views may be fifteen years later.

OTHER TYPES OF AGREEMENT

Before discussing situations more complex than simple licence agreements, consideration must be given to certain types of agreement other than licences, since some of these are liable to appear as components of the complete licensor/licensee relationship.

In Chapter 2 the application of the principles of contract law to *industrial property* was discussed. It should be borne in mind that the entities included in this practitioners' jargon expression are patents, know-how, registered trade marks and (not dealt with in this book) registered designs. Unlike other forms of property, these are all abstract in nature and it might be said that the essence of patents and registered trade marks is to create from an abstract or intellectual entity something which has the attributes of a piece of property. The contractual relations appropriate to such property have become reasonably well codified over the years and, as a very junior cousin, the law of confidential information has developed on the basis of the relationship between two persons, the giver and the receiver. More recently this has proved inadequate and it has been found necessary to regard industrial confidential information ("know-how" in this book) as a legal entity in its own right. The endeavour to fit this into a legal framework is still in a state of evolution and some of the contradictions arising from it (a recurring theme in the present work) can be seen in the analysis in Chapter 2 of a contrivance which is very popular at present with businessmen, the so-called "secrecy agreement."

For the businessman, a secrecy agreement tends to be a short cut to expressing in a document looking something like a contract a variety of more or less inchoate relationships which are not really legal relationships at all. They are all concerned with intellectual activities resulting in know-how, and a common factor of all of them is accordingly an undertaking to keep the relevant know-how secret. This being a clearly definable legal undertaking, there is a tendency to anchor the nomenclature to it and to call all agreements of the kind in question secrecy agreements. It can, however, be taken for granted here that agreements involving transfer of know-how always include a secrecy provision, and attention can, therefore, be concentrated on the main purpose of the agreement.

COLLABORATION AGREEMENTS

These were discussed in Chapter 2 in the context of contract law. They will now be considered from the point of view of the relationship between the parties. Four types will be considered: joint research by companies in a similar line of business, development by one party for a specified use of a product produced by the other, trials in a field of use of a range of chemical compounds produced by one of the parties, and development of plant to work a process invented by one of the parties.

Joint research agreements

The first thing to grasp is why the two companies, which are in a similar line of business and therefore presumably in competition, wish to collaborate. It is understandable that they can both get ahead faster if they pool their research, and it may be that what is really taking place is a merging of interests, an embryonic cartel. On the other hand there may be particular technological or geographical areas where the companies do not wish to compete, not because of any agreement between them, but for extraneous reasons. The classical case is that of companies located in different countries such as USA and UK, although such an example is hardly appropriate at present owing to the heavy pressure of anti-trust law against any such arrangement involving a US company. An example that one might think of in the technological field could be two rubber producers, one of which specialised in the tyre field and the other in all other rubber goods.

As explained in Chapter 2, the act of collaboration itself is not an appropriate subject for a contract. Only if the parties are prepared to agree on a commitment of, say, definite personnel or sums of money to their own research, can legal obligations be set up, but this is thought to be an unlikely situation. It is worth reiterating that the heart of the matter is a mutual undertaking that whatever research each party may do in a specified field will be fully communicated to the other — in other words, an exchange of know-how.

As also mentioned in Chapter 2, the reciprocal nature of the agreement avoids the difficulty inherent in trying to restrict the *mental* use of the information received from the other party. What is necessary, however, is to define the rights of the parties to use the know-how (and any patents which may have been generated) for *commercial* manufacture and sale. This generally amounts to letting each party have the exclusive right to exploit all the industrial property arising from the collaboration in his own geographical or technological area as the case may be.

If, however, no clear division of interests between the parties can be defined, each should have the joint right to exploit the industrial property as against third parties.

The form such arrangements should take — assignment, exclusive licensing, joint patents and so on — will be discussed in Chapter 6.

Specified use of a product

A situation of this kind can be illustrated by reference to a manufacturer of plastics who wishes to develop the use of a particular plastic to make moulded articles, and who seeks a collaborative arrangement with a fabricator. The real difficulty is that the plastics manufacturer wants to use the results to develop his sales of the plastic to all-comers whereas the fabricator wants to keep the results to himself. There are various ways in which this conflict may be resolved. Examples are:

1 The fabricator is given a lead time of x years, after which the plastics manufacturer is free to exploit the results.

2 The fabricator is given exclusive rights in a particular territory (made more easy if the plastic material is covered by a patent).

3 The industrial property residing in the fabricator's development work is licensed back to the plastics manufacturer in return for a payment, such as a royalty, to the fabricator.

Trials in a field of use

A typical case here is that of a chemical manufacturer producing almost as by-products of his research, a number of chemicals most of which remain as chemical curiosities. There is, however, a chance that one in a thousand of these chemicals may have a biological activity which, if developed, could lead to the use of the chemical as an insecticide or other pesticide, or as a drug. The realities of this situation are that the cost of taking a chemical to the point of marketing a successful pesticide is measured in £100 000s, and for a drug it is even greater. If the chemical manufacturer does not have the expertise or finance to put his chemicals through this sort of screening, he may seek an arrangement with a company specialising in the field. By this arrangement the manufacturer submits lists of candidate compounds and the specialist company undertakes to screen those which in its discretion it selects from the lists.

If a successful compound emerges, the rewards are very great indeed, but the contributions of the two companies are very disparate. The main reward which the chemical company is looking for is a monopoly in the supply of the chemical. This presents little difficulty if the chemical itself happens to be patentable, but if it is not — for example, because it has been described in the academic literature without reference to any biological activity — the manufacturer really needs an exclusive sales agreement. This, involving as it does matters of price, delivery and so on, is, however, impossible to settle at the time the collaboration agreement is negotiated, and the chemical manufacturer probably has to rely on the ethics of the screening company leading it to offer a reasonable deal when and if a successful compound emerges. This aspect is discussed more fully in a later chapter.

Development of plant

A company developing a process which requires special plant may wish to enter into a collaboration agreement with a plant manufacturer. If the only purchaser for the plant is the process company, the development of the plant will be a very expensive item. On the other hand the process company would not want the plant company to sell the plant freely to all-comers, since in so doing the plant company would be giving the process company's competitors free access to the new process. This difficulty can be resolved if the relevant industrial property is owned by the plant company and the process company is given a percentage of the proceeds obtained by selling the plant to third parties together with a licence under the industrial property.

PRELIMINARY OR ASSESSMENT AGREEMENTS

There is an inherent difficulty in licensing know-how, stemming from the fact that in order to interest the prospective licensee and enable him to put a valuation on the know-how it is necessary to make some disclosure of it, thus in effect jeopardising the property rights before any consideration has been negotiated. To overcome this difficulty it is necessary for the prospective licensee to sign a preliminary agreement. The essential terms of this agreement are an undertaking by the prospective licensee not to disclose the know-how to anyone else and an undertaking not to use it except for the purpose of assessing the desirability and value of a licence. The prospective licensor is entitled to ask for some consideration for disclosing the know-how if he thinks he can get it, which could take the form of a lump-sum payment. The parties could agree that this should be set against royalties if a licence is eventually negotiated. Part of the justification for monetary consideration is that (as explained earlier) with the best will in the world the person receiving the information cannot erase it from his mind if no licence is negotiated.

OPTION AGREEMENTS

Like secrecy agreements, offers of "options" are often bandied about as short cuts to establishing a relationship mistakenly believed to be legally effective, before the necessary basis of agreement has actually been arrived at. An option on, for example, a licence to be granted by *A* to *B* is a promise by *A* to grant *B* a licence if *B* so requests, on specified terms within a specified period or on the occurrence of a specified event. The important point is that at least the main terms of the licence must be specified in the option agreement; otherwise, as explained in Chapter 2, *A* would only have to put impossible terms on the eventual offer to make the option nugatory. There is, it is true, the possibility of a half-way house if *A*'s promise is to grant *B* a licence on "reasonable terms," or words to that effect, but like all obligations based on subjective concepts like reasonable, this can create more problems than it solves.

If the grant of an option is to amount to a legally binding contract, the "optionee" must give some consideration for the option which is stated in the option agreement. This, however, need be no more than nominal if that is what the parties want.

It will be seen that since an option requires advance negotiation of at least the main terms of the eventual licence, it is not often useful. Is there in fact any genuine half-way house between granting a licence and leaving the matter entirely open? The answer is the device popularly known as "first refusal," which consists in an agreement by the owner *A* of the industrial property to make *B* an offer of a licence within a given time or on the occurrence of a specified event. If *B* refuses this offer, *A* is entitled to make an offer to a third party, provided it is not on terms more favourable to the third party than were offered to *B*.

HIRING AGREEMENTS

This is a way of licensing a machine, or a process requiring a special machine. The patentee leases the machine, say, a document-copying machine, to users who pay rent for its use. For example, the machine could include a counter, the rent being payable per 100 copies taken. If the machine requires special paper which is itself patented, the return could be obtained on sales of the paper.

LICENSING SITUATIONS

The basic patent, trade-mark and know-how licences and other types of agreement which can be involved in licensing relationships have been discussed. Now it is necessary to look at a few typical situations that can arise in real life. It will be seen that agreements for these situations involve the basic patent licence with more or less elaboration, and sometimes with the addition in the same or a different document of the elements of the other types of agreement.

EXCLUSIVITY

In considering the patent licence in its simplest form, a situation was envisaged in which a manufacturer found that someone else's patent stood in the way of an operation he was engaged in or at least planning. He intended to operate in the patentee's area until he discovered the fence round it, and then all he wanted was the right to open the gate and go in without fear of an action for "trespassing." This right was the simple, non-exclusive licence discussed earlier in this chapter.

Another type of situation is one in which the licensed operation would be a new departure for the licensee, requiring investment in development, plant and promotion. In such a case the prospective licensee is not likely to embark on the venture unless the patentee can give him some assurances regarding the grant of licences to third parties. In other words he will want at least some measure of exclusivity.

Full exclusivity

In this case the patentee not only renounces the right to grant further licences but also the right to operate under the patent himself. Since a manufacturing firm is in business to manufacture and sell, why should it be prepared to grant such an exclusive licence? The most common reason is territorial. The patentee may find it more profitable, allowing for the considerations discussed in the last chapter, to license his innovation in one or more foreign countries than to attempt to set up a manufacturing operation. If such a decision to license is made, the patentee may lose little by formally renouncing his own right to manufacture in the territory.

It should be noted that the patent system is well suited to this kind of territorial division, since a patent runs only in its own country and there is no legal or practical difficulty in associating different kinds of licence rights with different patents — that is, different countries. (This will not apply to the European Common Market if present plans for a common patent system fructify.) The position is very different if the industrial property which is being licensed does not include a patent, since a division of territory then depends on restrictions accepted by contract between the parties rather than on statutory rights granted separately by the state apparatus of the respective countries, and such contractual restrictions are unlawful in many parts of the world.

Another situation in which the patentee may be willing to grant an exclusive licence arises when the patent is part of a collaboration arrangement. It will be obvious that, in some of the collaboration situations discussed above, the grant of an exclusive licence to the collaborating party is the only viable outcome of the collaboration.

An exclusive licence may also be ceded without too much misgiving in cases (usually of subsidiary importance) in which, although the patentee has decided not to operate the invention himself, another company in the same line of business arrives at a different decision. There may be special reasons, not strictly economic, for this difference of view, or the patentee company may just have made a faulty decision. If another company then asks for a licence it may be too late or too difficult for the patentee to reverse its previous decision not to operate, and it may be glad to turn the situation to advantage by granting an exclusive licence.

The reasons for granting exclusivity, discussed above presuppose that manufacture under the patent is in the patentee's own line of business. This, however, is not so if the patentee is a non-manufacturing organisation (discussed in Chapter 7). It may also occasionally happen that a manufacturing company makes an invention outside its own line of business. In these cases an exclusive licence is likely to be the best way of exploiting the invention.

Exclusive right to make, non-exclusive to sell
This is often part of a territorial deal. It means that an exclusive manufacturing licence can be granted in each of a number of countries, without any restriction on the right of each licensee to export all over the world.

Exclusivity limited to a technological field
It is possible to grant an exclusive licence which is limited, or the exclusivity of which is limited, to a particular technological field within the area covered by the patent. A good example of different fields within the patented area is the one mentioned above in which the invention relates to a new synthetic rubber. The use of the rubber for automotive tyres on the one hand and domestic goods on the other are distinct fields from the technical and commercial points of view. The patentee is free to grant an exclusive licence in one field and one or more non-exclusive licences in the other.

Partial exclusivity
This arises where the special prerequisites for an exclusive licence are absent, but the patentee is nevertheless willing to limit the number of licences he will grant. In legal terms it means that the patentee enters into an undertaking or "covenant" with each licensee that he will not grant more than *x* number of licences. It is impossible to generalise on the situations in which this sort of arrangement is viable, if only because they are rather unusual. It is a compromise of a kind which is acceptable to the parties only in special circumstances.

Sole licence

This is a special case of partial exclusivity in which the patentee in effect covenants with a licensee that he will grant only the one licence. It differs from an exclusive licence in that the patentee retains the right to operate the invention himself. The patentee and the sole licensee are thus effectively in competition. It will be apparent that here also the circumstances in which such an arrangement is satisfactory are limited.

THE TERMS OF EXCLUSIVE LICENCES

The grant of an exclusive licence virtually puts the exclusive licensee in the shoes of the patentee. In the UK he acquires a statutory status which enables him to do nearly all the things a patentee can do, most importantly to sue for infringement of the patent. What, then, is the difference between granting an exclusive licence to someone and assigning the patent (that is, transferring the ownership of it) to him? The real difference lies in the possibility of bringing the exclusive licence to an end, which is a matter for negotiation along with the other terms on which the licence is granted.

Minimum royalty

The royalty terms on which an exclusive licence may be granted are a matter for negotiation just as they are in the case of a non-exclusive licence, but there is one basic difference. Since the patentee is putting all his eggs in one basket he is entitled to ask the licensee for a minimum below which royalty payments in a given period, usually a year, will not fall. The licensee, for his part, is buying not only the freedom of entry into the fenced-off area, but the fence as well; in other words he is acquiring the monopoly and the right to enforce it. It is therefore reasonable that he should make some specified payment over and above a royalty on use of the invention. It is accordingly usual for an exclusive licensee to pay an "annual minimum royalty." This can either be an outright undertaking, so that failure to pay would be a breach of the contract, or the licensee can be free not to pay the minimum, subject to a penalty which could either be termination of the licence or its conversion into a non-exclusive licence.

If setting a royalty rate is difficult, fixing an annual minimum is even more so since it involves an extra unknown — the performance of the licensee. The difficulty can be mitigated to some extent by postponing the liability to pay at any rate the full annual minimum, until, say, two or three years after the granting of the licence, but as pointed out in Chapter 2, it is still necessary to fix the amount at the date of the original agreement, since without this no firm bargain has been struck.

Other performance guarantees

An annual minimum royalty is really a guarantee by the licensee that he will attain a minimum level of performance in operating the licence, and it is usually the most effective and convenient way of making such a guarantee. Other possibilities are, however, available. For instance the licensee may undertake to achieve a stated minimum volume of production per year, or to erect at least *x* number of plants in different geographical or technological areas.

Another type of provision which is often seen (certainly in all the books of precedents) is that the licensee will "use his best endeavours" to produce and sell the patented article or product. Such clauses, however, have little real meaning. How much effort and money must the licensee put into a product which turns out to be unsatisfactory before he has discharged his obligations? No one can say. Perhaps slightly better is an undertaking to use all reasonable endeavours, but it would seem that this adds nothing to what the licensee would normally do in any case in his own interest. It does, however, prevent a dog-in-the-manger attitude by the licensee of failure to operate the invention for reasons unconnected with the marketability of the product, including sheer slackness. But it is not until the parties have struck a bargain in terms of some quantitative measure of performance that any real commitment has been made.

Sub-licences

The right to grant sub-licences tends to be a natural part of an exclusive licence, although it can arise in various kinds of non-exclusive deal as well. Unless a sub-licensing right is provided for in the contract, the licensee does not have it. The licensee would normally like to have the right, as it gives him an added degree of freedom. In the case of an exclusive licence, the licensor will probably feel the same way, as a sub-licensing right will increase the possibilities open to the licensee for exploiting the invention, and thus contribute to the licensor's ever-present preoccupation with securing adequate performance by his exclusive licensee.

Depending on a variety of circumstances, the licensor may be content to leave the licensee entirely free to carry out his own sub-licensing policy, or the licensor may seek to retain some measure of control. For instance, he may try to get agreement that he must give prior approval to any sub-licensee or even to the terms of the sub-licence, or that he will be notified of the grant of a sub-licence and possibly be sent a copy of the agreement.

Infringement of the licensed patent

This was dealt with at some length on pages 73-4 and most of what was written there applies equally to exclusive licences. There is a difference, however, in that the exclusive licensee has a greater interest in suppressing infringement. He has his own remedy, since he can sue for infringement in his own name, nevertheless it would be reasonable for the licensee to be able not only to suspend royalty payments until the infringement had been suppressed, but also to use the suspended royalties to defray his expenses in taking action against the infringer. After all, it is the licensor's patent he is upholding.

What is the position if neither the licensor nor the licensee wishes to take legal action? If the licence is non-exclusive it is always open to the licensor to "abate" the infringement by granting the infringer a licence, but this is not possible with an exclusive licence unless the licensee agrees. The licensor may attempt to get this agreement written into the contract, but he is unlikely to succeed because the grant of a licence to the infringer could change the whole basis of the agreement. All that can be done, therefore, is for the licensor and licensee to try to negotiate some new deal, royalty payments being meanwhile suspended for a stated period of time, say one or two years.

The same principles apply to sole or partially exclusive licences, except for the technicality that the licensee cannot sue the infringer in his own name. Provision must therefore be made for the licensor to lend his name to the licensee if the latter is willing to take action and the former is not.

EXCLUSIVE TRADE-MARK LICENCE

It was stated above that a simple non-exclusive trade-mark licence is unlikely to make commercial sense. This is not, however, true of an exclusive licence, since the latter does not detract from the characteristic feature of a trade-mark that it should be used by only one supplier. Even so, situations where the grant of a trade-mark licence is appropriate are not very common. Usually the transaction would be part of a wider relationship of a kind discussed later in this chapter.

EXCLUSIVITY IN KNOW-HOW AGREEMENTS

This heading is something of a contradiction in terms. A licensor of know-how can never undertake that the licensee will have an exclusive position. The most he can do is to promise not to disclose the know-how to, or permit its use by, any other person, but this undertaking is of no practical value if third parties acquire the know-how otherwise than from the licensor. Its worth is therefore very much less than that of an exclusive licence under a patent.

MANUFACTURING INVENTION: NON-EXCLUSIVE LICENSING POLICY

It is useful in considering licensing policy to classify inventions as "manufacturing" and "user" inventions. A manufacturing invention in this terminology is one whose operation is in the line of business of the patentee and his competitors. In other words the fenced-off area represented by the "claim" of the patent is an article, machine or product, or process of making it, which would fit into the patentee's own type of manufacturing operation.

A user invention is one whose operation is in the line of business of the patentee's customers, namely one which the patentee has developed as an aid to the sale of one of his products. The most usual type of user invention is a new application of a product — for example, the use of a chemical for the treatment of textiles — although it is conceivable that it could be a new way of using a machine or plant.

High patent, low know-how content

So far as manufacturing inventions are concerned, it will be apparent that the normal situation is for the patentee to use the patent as a protection for his own manufacture. A licensing policy would be dictated only by special circumstances, as discussed in the last chapter. The present section is concerned with the case in which the patentee has made a development destined to displace an existing process in virtually the whole of the industry because it leads to a markedly superior product or to the same product at a markedly reduced price. The new glass-making process mentioned in the last chapter is an example. Here the patentee is faced with the sheer impossibility of satisfying the whole market from his own resources or of stemming the tide of imitators by asserting his legal rights. He therefore decides to make a virtue of necessity by granting licences to his competitors.

Clearly this situation points to a non-exclusive licensing policy. It also indicates that the process is known to be a commercial success, with the corollary that the patentee is likely to have generated substantial know-how in developing it. The patentee will therefore probably wish to complete the licensing job and maximise his return by offering know-how licences along with the patent licences.

The deal will thus be a simple non-exclusive patent licence and know-how licence. Both, of course, can be included in the same agreement. The royalty will reflect the importance of the innovation and the fact that know-how is included.

There will probably be a substantial downpayment in consideration of both the initial transfer of know-how and the privilege of joining the "club."

The patentee will probably want to standardise the terms for all licensees. This can be done, in general, only if the patentee is in a strong enough position to adopt a take-it-or-leave-it attitude to new licensees — which he will be in the present situation. His negotiating strength will be enhanced if he issues a printed licence agreement, thus making it clear at the outset that alterations are not expected.

Will there be any provision for licensing improvements or for a continuing transfer of know-how? Presumably the patentee would prefer not, so that if he makes any important development he has the choice of keeping it to himself or getting some further advantage in return for adding it to the licences. Minor developments could be offered free, thus cementing the goodwill between the parties, which would not be possible if the original agreements already *obliged* the patentee to furnish improvements.

High know-how, low patent content

The case just described is one in which the licensee is relying mainly on his patent position, know-how being thrown in, as it were, to complete the job. The real novelty is in the original idea for (in the example) making glass by the new technique. A certain amount of information about the plant and process parameters for putting the idea into practice must have been given in the patent specification which had been or would shortly be published. The remaining practical details, although valuable, are secondary.

It is indeed possible to make a rough generalisation that in a given innovation the patent content and know-how content tend to be in inverse proportion. This is partly because the more one puts into a patent specification the less is left over as know-how (always remembering that, in the sense in which the term is used here, know-how is restricted to *confidential* information), and partly because the further an innovation is ahead of its time the greater its degree of patentability but the less its content of practical operating detail. The recent case of Valensi *v* British Radio

Corporation ([1971] *Fleet Street Law Reports*, page 66) is an excellent example. The inventor conceived of the basic idea of separate colour and brightness signals for colour television in 1938. His patent (extended twice, for war loss and inadequate remuneration) was found valid and infringed by leading systems in use today. However, this generalisation should not be pressed too far, and no doubt there are many exceptions to it.

A case in which the know-how content is likely to be more significant than the patent is that of a plant contractor designing plant for carrying out a chemical process which is basically known but which had not hitherto been put into practice. Given the process, the work of the plant designer is not likely to lead to any unobvious idea which can be isolated and made the subject of a patent. The outcome consists rather of the arrangement and coordination of known parts (such as pumps, pipes, valves, centrifuges and autoclaves) and a control system programmed in a known manner in accordance with the process parameters. All this will be put together in a book giving drawings, dimensions and the rest, which will be of considerable value so long as it remains confidential — but is not likely to contain any patentable inventions. If there is a patent it will probably be for some process detail (temperature, pressure, catalyst) which is a factor in converting the chemical process from an academic curiosity into a workable industrial operation. The inventor probably regards it as a key factor, but in practice it all too often happens that a determined competitor can juggle with the process as a whole and produce a set of parameters which does not involve the "key factor."

At all events the plant contractor who wishes to license others may well find that the more valuable part of what he has to offer is the book containing the know-how, together with technical assistance by staff loaned to the licensee. Having arrived at this point, however, it is found that the form of the deal is basically similar to that in the case in which the patent is the more important item. In both, there is the grant of a non-exclusive licence under the patent and a licence to use the know-how. What is different is the relative importance of the terms of the contract belonging to the patent and those belonging to the know-how. (These were discussed in some detail on pages 35-6.)

A good deal of technical writing may be involved in an agreement for licensing substantial know-how because of the detail involved in such matters as the definition of the know-how, the method of rendering technical assistance and the technical performance guarantees given by the licensor. A number of specimen agreements have been published in the technical literature.

USER INVENTIONS

Manufacturers often carry out applicational research to find new or improved uses for their products. If such a use is patentable, the objective of the manufacturer is normally to use the patent to give him a privileged, if not a monopoly, position in supplying the product for the patented use. It has been suggested previously, however, that to use a patent in this way is fraught with legal restrictions and prohibitions. The nature of these is part of the law of the various countries and therefore differs from one to another. The technicalities of the provisions will be discussed in the next chapter; for the moment it is enough to say briefly that the philosophy behind them is that the monopoly position accorded by the grant of a patent ought not to extend beyond the fenced-off area of the patent claims. Thus, while the patentee can legitimately exact a consideration for a licence to enter this area, this consideration must not be such as to add a further monopoly or part-monopoly to the one already granted.

So, what kind of relationships in fact emerge between the owner of a patent for a process of using an unpatented material and his customer? To answer this in any significant way it is best to deal with a specific country, and the UK is the best one to start with for various reasons. The following discussion is therefore to be read as applying to the UK, and the matter will be taken up in relation to other countries in the next chapter.

Informal or tacit licences

Whatever the law may say, there is a widespread belief among businessmen that if *B* buys *x* from the owner *A* of the patent he will not risk legal action, whereas if he buys *x* elsewhere he will be in jeopardy. It is indeed true that if *B* (who buys from *A*) and *C* (who buys elsewhere) are both infringing the patent, *A* can elect to sue *C* and leave *B* alone. So long as *B* is content to leave the matter like that, all is well, but if he seeks an assurance from *A*, that assurance cannot lawfully be given since it would amount to telling *B* that he has a licence so long as he purchases from *A*. In making such an agreement, *A* would run the risk of his patent becoming unenforceable. The assurance cannot lawfully be given but it no doubt often is.

Take, as an example, a patent for the use of *x* as a weedkiller. *A*'s sales representative knows that his company owns this patent and that he can use it to persuade farmers to buy *x* from *A*. He is likely at least to hint that if the farmer wants to buy elsewhere he may be in difficulties under the patent. If the farmer understands the law or takes advice he can snap his fingers at the salesman since what the latter has said amounts to a veiled offer of a licence on condition that *x* is purchased from *A*. Generally, however, the farmer will not take this attitude even if he is fully aware of the legal position, and thus it can be said that the relationship between *A* and the farmer is viable.

This viability rests on a reasonable sales policy by *A*, involving a price for *x* which, while including a premium in recognition of the patent, nevertheless keeps this at a modest amount so that the overall price is not greedy.

A also offers technical advice on the use of *x*, so that, in effect, *A* is tacitly granting a licence under the patent and know-how (in the guise of technical service) in return for a royalty. The royalty consists of a premium on the price, which the customer probably does not realise is there, until he seeks a quotation from another supplier. So long as all this appears reasonable to the farmer, he will be content to accept it. If he does so, the arrangement is viable because neither party wants to upset it and it is highly unlikely that any other person will get to know about it, at any rate with the degree of certainty necessary to rely on it in a court of law as a defence against *A*'s patent.

Formal licences under user patents

The approach described above ceases to be viable if the customer/licensee *B* requires some continuing assurance of a licence, for instance if he is himself an industrialist who wants to use the patented process on a substantial scale in his own manufacture. This might happen, for example, if *B* has an oil refinery and wants to use an unpatented catalyst in a refining process which is the subject of a patent owned by *A*. In such circumstances, *B* will not be content with the casual arrangements that would satisfy someone like a farmer in a small way of business. Another case in which a formal licence is required arises when the use of the material *x* involves undertakings by the user, such as quality control.

Considering the oil refiner first, the law permits *A* to make a licence conditional on purchase of the catalyst from *A* provided that at the same time *B* has an option to purchase elsewhere on "reasonable" terms. This represents a compromise which is satisfactory to *B*, but less so to *A*. Other compromise ways of dealing with the situation which are described in the next chapter include "label licensing" — an arrangement which tends to favour *A* rather than *B*.

User licences involving quality control

A special case arises when a user invention consists in a process for treating goods sold to the ultimate consumer, and the patentee wishes to establish the process by way of a quality control extending to the goods retailed to the public. As examples we can mention treatments for finishing textile fabrics and processes for plating or polishing metal articles.

Considering the textile-finishing case, the essence of the arrangement is that the patentee, who supplies the unpatented material *x*, licences a number of textile-finishing companies to operate the process, for example for flameproofing or waterproofing the fabric. It is in the general interest that the treatment and the treated fabric should become known to the public by a trade mark and that it should be subject to a uniform quality control. The patentee *A*, therefore, devises and registers a trade mark and requires each licensee to use this mark on all the treated fabric. The agreement requires samples to be submitted to *A* who has the right to veto the sale of substandard material. As a refinement, *A* issues labels in just sufficient quantity to label the garments or the like made from approved fabric and in this way the control can be carried through from the finisher to the garment maker.

In this arrangement it is implicit that each finisher has a licence to use the registered trade mark, and this is legitimate in view of the quality control provisions. It is desirable to issue the licences as formal documents which can be used as a basis for making the licensees "registered users" under the Trade Marks Act.

The scheme just described is likely to be viable only if the invention in question is of a pioneer character or gives superlative quality to the treated goods. Once the outstanding nature of the innovation is undermined by competition, it is likely that competitors of *A* who supply materials for competing finishes will sell them "licence-free" — that is, without the grant of a formal licence agreement. The obligation of such a supplier will then be limited to giving normal technical service, and *A*'s elaborate control scheme will be eroded and eventually become uncompetitive.

TECHNOLOGICAL PARTNERSHIP

The sort of situation envisaged here is one in which a company is pioneering a new sector of technology and wishes to set up a kind of junior partner, usually in a different geographical area. In the late 1940s and 1950s such "partnerships" between a US pioneer and a licensee in, say the UK or Germany were fairly common, but they are less so now, partly because of the readiness of US companies to set up a manufacturing operation abroad and partly because of the increasing restrictions of US anti-trust law on any form of collaboration.

An example of what was referred to above as a new sector of technology might be the solid-state electronic materials referred to in Chapter 3, or a new class of chemical compounds. In both cases there would be great scope for development in devising variants of the substances themselves and processes for making them, and in ramifying applications, in one case to electronic equipment and in the other to a variety of uses from weedkillers to plastics.

Exclusive licences

It would be natural in such a situation that the licence should be exclusive in the licensee's territory. The agreement would thus be based on a composite of exclusive patent and know-how and possibly also trade-mark licences. But it would be more than that. An attempt would be made to provide for a thoroughgoing collaboration between the parties. The essential part of this would be a continuing exchange of know-how, and of patent licences under new developments patented during the agreement.

Definition of field of agreement

If an agreement is to provide that know-how and patents arising in the future are to be handed over to the other party, it is important to define without any chance of misunderstanding the field of technology to which this undertaking applies. An example of what could go wrong would be a definition in an agreement between *A* and *B* referring to a treatment of "fabrics made of wool." If *A* makes an invention involving the application of the treatment to carpets, he may argue that it is not within the agreement because carpets are not fabrics. *B* on the other hand maintains that carpets are fabrics, if not in ordinary parlance, at least in the context of the agreement. After all, says *B*, this dealt with a treatment applicable to wool and it did not matter whether it was in the form of a fabric in the narrower sense or of a carpet.

The dispute could have been avoided if the parties had been more thorough in thinking out the possibilities when the agreement was being negotiated. They could then have resolved the issue by referring to "fabrics made of wool including (or not including) carpets." Even if one of the parties did not have his way (which does not necessarily follow, since the boot would have been on the other foot if *B* had made the carpet invention), a clear definition would at least have avoided the unpleasantness of a dispute.

Drafting a definition of the technological field is much the same sort of exercise as drafting a patent claim. Both are endeavours to extrapolate from the particular matter which is being considered by the negotiators or the inventor to as wide a range of possibilities as can be envisaged and then map out in words the appropriate technological area. Indeed it is not uncommon to define the field of an agreement as being the scope of the claims (actually the broadest claim) of a patent. This, however, is more often than not a substitute for, rather than the result of, clear thinking about what the definition should be. This is especially so if the definition refers to a number of patents, unless it is made clear that the field is the area bounded by the fence which encloses all the patents collectively, but even so this would be an unsatisfactory hotch-potch.

A common pitfall is the use of the word "improvement," beloved of the classical draftsman and the books of precedents. More will be said on this and other details of drafting in Chapter 6.

Exchange of know-how

There is little more to be said on this subject, which has been dealt with above in slightly different contexts. The provisions will normally be reciprocal, except that if the licensee *B* has not previously operated in the field, only *A* need undertake to furnish all know-how available at the date of the agreement. It is desirable to specify the forms, methods and times of transmission of the information, since there is a tendency for slackness to creep in, especially when the honeymoon period of the collaboration has passed.

The agreement will normally provide that information furnished by *A* will be kept secret by *B* and vice versa. Since the arrangement is exclusive, it should also provide that information is to be kept secret by the donor as well as by the recipient.

Exchange of patent rights

If an agreement provides for a continuing transmission of know-how, it ought logically to make provision for any patentable invention which may arise, although the converse is not necessarily true. This is because patentable inventions are inevitably included among the transmitted know-how, whereas patented inventions can be communicated without any unpatented know-how.

The minimum which is required is for *B* to have the right to use *A*'s inventions in *B*'s territory and vice versa. The parties may, however, go beyond this by agreeing that such rights shall be exclusive, or even that *A* shall assign the patents outright to *B* and vice versa in the respective territories. Another possibility is for *A* or *B* to give the other the right of "first refusal" of a licence, but this would be more appropriate in "neutral" territory — that is, in territory not allocated to *A* or *B*.

It will be appreciated that changes can be rung on these possibilities, and these are dealt with more fully in Chapter 6.

It is worth noting that the grant of a licence from *B* to *A* in return for a licence or licences from *A* to *B* in this kind of agreement is a particular case of "cross-licensing." The simplest type of cross-licence is an agreement in which *A* licences *B* under a patent in return simply for a licence from *B* under one of *B*'s patents.

Royalty provisions

Of course the latter arrangement would not be appropriate to the present type of agreement, since even if *B* generates patents, the benefits of the agreement are not reciprocal. *A* had the initial patent(s) and know-how and has effectively set *B* up in this line of business. He will therefore expect a continuing royalty from *B*, although the parties may agree that this may be partly offset by an agreed royalty payable under any future patent generated by *B*. The royalty from *B* to *A* may be based on all *B*'s operations within the field, or only on those falling within one of *A*'s patents. On the other hand *A*'s royalty to *B* (if any is provided for) would be based only on *B*'s patents.

Duration

Whenever a know-how licence is combined with a patent licence the question of termination has to be carefully considered. The considerations applying to these types of licence separately have already been discussed. Normally the patent licence will last for the life of the patent, but if new patents are being generated during the agreement, they may extend its life to an undesirable extent.

Moreover, it is possible that the parties do not wish the know-how provisions to be conterminous with the patent licence. If they wish the former to be of longer duration they are in difficulty with *s*58 of the Patents Act (mentioned above) since this applies to all agreements relating to a licence under a patent (see page 125).

It is more likely, however, that the parties will want the know-how provisions to be of shorter duration. One way of coping with these problems is to specify an active life and a passive life for the agreement. During the active life (which might, for instance, be ten years), all the provisions remain in force but thereafter, during the passive life, only the licences under patents then existing, and the terms relevant thereto, remain in force. This gets over the difficulty that the agreement could otherwise be extended indefinitely as new patents are added (subject to *s*58 for UK patents), and also restricts the period during which collaboration has to be maintained, possibly against the wishes of one of the parties.

Chapter 5

Legal restraints on licence agreements

Chapter 4 described the kinds of agreement that a prospective licensor and licensee may wish to negotiate in various types of situation. In most countries, however, a measure of restraint is imposed by statute and case law on the arrangements which negotiating parties may lawfully make with each other. This chapter surveys the types of restraint operating in most of the countries which are significant from a licensing point of view. The approach, as always in this book, being to explain the situation in broad terms to the businessman or manager so that he may know the sort of thing he is up against and where he needs to tread warily — with the assistance of his professional advisers.

An indication of what is involved in legal restraints on licence agreements was given in the previous chapter in a warning note about danger areas under US anti-trust law, and also in discussing restrictions on the source of supply of unpatented raw materials. It was stated that the UK was perhaps the least severe of the main industrial countries

(Scandinavia excepted) so that the full gamut of licensing terms could be discussed in relation to this country, and this would form a basis for a description of restraints applying to some of the terms in other countries. It is convenient now to go to the other extreme, namely the restrictions imposed by anti-trust law in the USA, after which there is a brief survey of other countries which, in the main, take an intermediate position.

US anti-trust law is a complex and technical subject. Many volumes have been written about it, but all that is necessary here is a summary of the highlights, the erection of a few signposts, to guide the businessman to an appreciation of the sort of terms that may and may not be included in his licensing deal in the States.

OBJECTIVES OF US ANTI-TRUST LAW

The objectives of anti-trust law applied to licensing may be described as:

1 To prevent the use of the patent monopoly in such a way as to create generalised monopolistic situations or to create specific new monopolies not commensurate with the "fenced-off area" of the patent
2 To prevent arrangements which result in collaboration or a diminution of competition between competitors
3 To prevent the concept established by the patent system of property rights in "inventions" from encroaching on other creations of the mind such as unpatented and unpatentable know-how

Many of the wrongs committed under anti-trust law, especially in relation to the first of the above objectives, are called "misuse of the patent," which is in a sense the counterpart (though very different in its effect) of the "abuse of monopoly" which is part of the law in the UK and other countries. The latter is discussed later (pages 133-5) in the present chapter although it does not, in contradistinction to the US "misuse of patent", have a direct bearing on the terms of licence agreements.

US anti-trust law involves evaluation of given situations in terms of a very widely expressed prohibition of monopoly. It is therefore the spirit that counts, rather than any specifically formulated rules. It is thought best, however, to begin by setting out the particular practices which have been, or are likely to be held to be, unlawful so that a discussion of the broader aspects of the law can be approached with a better understanding of what is involved.

GENERAL MONOPOLISTIC SITUATIONS

These are situations in which the power of patent property is used to establish the domination of one company or a group of companies over an industry. This sort of situation was at the root of a handful of important anti-trust cases following the Second World War. By its nature such a violation of the law tends to be blatant and therefore clear enough when it happens. No doubt, however, there are cases in which the situation could develop gradually over a period of years and it would therefore be prudent for the owner of important patent rights to have the possibility at the back of his mind in all decisions regarding the exploitation of the rights, so that he does not unwittingly drift into a dangerous position.

The power of patents

The nature of patents is such that the strength of a patent position covering a particular development — for example, transistors or a method of glass-making — increases disproportionately with the number of patents involved. It is unusual for a development to be covered by a single impregnable dominant patent. It is, however, not uncommon for the originator to obtain one patent after another, each for relatively small steps or parts of the development. Together they cover a large technological area and while the validity of any one of them may be suspect, the sheer labour of assessing all of them may be enough to deter a would-be challenger.

If, now, the owner of the "web" of patents exerts to the full the power it has given him, he may *ipso facto* be in danger of violating anti-trust law, because he is relying on something over and above a *valid* patent or patents (which would represent a genuine advance in technology), namely on the difficulty of detecting and proving the *invalidity* of one or more of the total collection.

Collusive arrangements

Just as the danger of violation tends to increase disproportionately with the number of patents, so it does with the number of "persons" (normally, corporate bodies) involved. While it may be legitimate for one company, which is sufficiently scrupulous about its methods, to achieve a dominating position by its own efforts, it can seldom if ever be lawful for this result to be achieved by collusion between two or more companies.

Cross-licensing

The usual method by which such collusion is brought about is by cross-licensing — that is, the grant by company *A* of a licence under one or more patents to *B* in return for the grant of licences by *B* to *A*. In itself there is no harm in cross-licensing, but it can be used to establish the joint dominance of *A* and *B* in an industry, and then it becomes unlawful. It was a major element in some of the big anti-trust suits referred to above, such as United States *v* Line Materials Co (1948), Hartford Empire *v* United States (1945) and United States *v* General Electric (Lamps) (1949).

Patent pool

This is a particular form of cross-licensing in which a number of companies license each other under all their patents in one field of technology, such as computers. If it is just this and nothing more, it may be lawful. Usually, however, the object is to have some kind of royalty arrangement not specifically tied to individual patents, to exclude non-pool members from the benefits of the arrangement, and to ensure that all future patents of pool members come into the pool. All these objects are highly suspect, and it is a fair assumption that any patent pool involving them is unlawful in the USA.

Exclusivity

At the present time, the grant of an exclusive licence is not in itself unlawful, but it would clearly be an aggravating factor in any situation tending towards monopolisation or dominance.

SPECIFIC TERMS SUSPECT UNDER ANTI-TRUST LAWS

Stepping down from the Olympian heights of industry-dominating situations, we now consider a number of practices that tend to recur in licensing and which have been or are likely to be held to be unlawful because they amount to "misuse of the patent" or are in restraint of trade. The difference between these categories lies in the penalties or sanctions which may be applied (see below).

The word "suspect" appearing in the section heading has been used deliberately. It is of the essence of US anti-trust law that it provides no enumeration of unlawful practices. Whether a particular provision of an agreement is lawful or not depends primarily on the overall nature of the agreement and its context. It is, however, possible to say with certainty that, whatever the context, certain licensing terms are bound to be unlawful. One can safely say that among these is any attempt to use the licence to *control prices*, although oddly enough, owing to a judgement favourable to the patentee in United States *v* General Electric Co there is some legal obscurity on the authority for this statement. This case was decided in 1926 and the virtually unanimous view of informed opinion is that it would be reversed by the Supreme Court today.

Tying clauses

Another definitely unlawful practice, often known as a "tying clause", is to make the grant of a licence conditional on the purchase of unpatented raw material from a specified source (usually the patentee). The circumstances in which this can arise were described at some length in Chapter 4 and the consequences in terms of UK law and commercial practice were discussed. The law and practice are different in the USA in several respects, some of which will appear when the general aspects of anti-trust law and the detail of the UK law on the subject are dealt with. For the moment, specific aspects of the US law will be considered.

As just stated, tying clauses in their crude form are always unlawful. So also are clauses which provide for a differential royalty rate depending on whether the unpatented material is bought from the patentee or a third party. The question arises whether any practice which gives any kind of advantage to the patentee as a supplier of an unpatented material can be lawful. The answer at the present date is "no." At one time it was thought to be lawful to make a licence agreement under which the licensee could purchase either from the patentee at a price including a reasonable royalty, or from a third party on paying the same royalty to the patentee. This could give a slight edge to the patentee since purchase from him would save the customer a certain amount of administrative and accounting work. The practice is now considered unlawful except, perhaps, where the licensees are large companies with adequate service facilities to whom the extra work would not be significant. What it amounts to is, that if it is worth doing it is unlawful.

On the other hand there have recently been a few cases going against the tide, in which the Court has held that the patented process needed an unpatented material of very high quality, so that it would be to the patentee's detriment if the licensee obtained the material from an uncontrolled source. Similar cases have arisen with respect to trade-mark licences. It is thought, however, that such cases should be regarded as exceptions to the general rule, based on their own special facts.

Contributory infringement

Paradoxically, US patent law has a provision, known as "contributory infringement," which is favourable to the owner of a user patent, but is absent from the UK law. According to *s*271(*b*) and (*c*) of the Patent Statute it is an infringement of a patent actively to induce infringement by someone else or to sell unpatented components or materials knowing that they are especially adapted for use in infringement of the patent. In theory this should enable the patentee to sue a competitor for supplying the raw material but in practice such action might well be held to contravene anti-trust law, notwithstanding the provisions of the Patent Statute. It would, however, be lawful to grant him a licence in return for royalty or other consideration. But this, in general, is not what the patentee wants. He wants to be able to stop the competitor from supplying this raw material, but the contributory infringement section has a serious limitation in that the simple supply of the unpatented material (that is, with no active inducement to infringe — for example, by supplying data sheets) is an infringement only if the unpatented material is not a "staple commodity of commerce suitable for substantial non-infringing use." This greatly narrows the useful effect of the provision to materials which, although not staple commodities, are yet not novel in themselves, because if they were novel they would be patentable in their own right and the patent could be used to stop their manufacture and sale; hence the tying clause problem would not arise. An example might be the use of a substance *X* as a catalyst in making sulphuric acid. There are three possibilities:

1 *X* is new and patentable, in which case no problem arises
2 *X* is known and is a staple commodity for some other purpose, in which case there is no lawful way of getting a privileged position in its supply
3 *X* is known but is not a staple commodity, in which case some measure of control can be exercised over its supply under the contributory infringement provision

Exhaustion of patent rights

It is not lawful for a patentee or licensee to attach any restrictions to the use or resale of a patented article or product after its first sale. First and foremost this applies to control of resale price, but it is of general application. For example, a patentee cannot make a licence to manufacture and sell a therapeutic substance dependent on the licensee's customers reselling the material as a formulated pharmaceutical, rather than in bulk. It is worth noting here that even the right to prevent the licensee himself from selling in bulk is currently being attacked.

Improvement patents

Although not yet definitely unlawful, it is likely that licences providing for the grant back to the licensor of exclusive rights in improvement patents will soon be held to be a violation of anti-trust law, presumably on the basis that they extend the tie-up between licensor and licensee to future unknown fields of activity.

Territorial division

This is definitely out, except on the basis of valid patent rights. Thus it is lawful in itself to withhold a licence under one or more of the non-US equivalents of a US patent, thus effectively limiting the licensee's right to export. However, even this practice will be a violation if it is shown to be part of a wider scheme for a territorial division of markets.

Technological division

Is it lawful to restrict a licence to a particular technological area within the total area of the patent? If the situation is like the one mentioned earlier, where the patent covers a type of rubber and its use for tyres is a different business from that for other goods, it has up to now been legitimate to give a licence to a company restricted to one or other of these fields, though a current case casts doubt on this assertion. If, however, the patent were for an additive for petrol and lubricating oil, it might well be (or may in the future become) unlawful to license an oil company *A* for petrol only and another oil company *B* for lubricating oil only. On the other hand it is legitimate to charge a licensee different royalties for different fields of use.

Royalty for set of patents

It is not legitimate to use one patent to make a licensee take a licence under one or more other patents. This is relevant to the practice of including a number of patents in an agreement and charging the same royalty for the use of any or all of them. As the law now stands, a prospective licensee must effectively have the option of reducing the number of patents under which he is licensed and at the same time reducing the royalty — if not proportionately, at least to a significant extent. In view of the complex interrelation of patent rights, this restriction may not always be of great potential importance. If, for example, the set of patents is such that the actual article or product manufactured by the licensee falls within all of them, and the royalty is chargeable on that article or product, the question does not arise.

If, on the other hand, there are, say, two mutually exclusive patents covering different designs of a product, then it would be reasonable to regard the deal as two separate licences in one agreement, with the patents probably equal in value and worth, say, a royalty of 5 per cent each. Clearly in such a case only the one royalty rate is quoted in the agreement.

Patent and trade-mark deal

A somewhat similar point arises when a patentee wants to use his patent to make his licensee use his (the patentee's) trade mark. It is unlawful to do this, and the licensee should be offered two separate agreements. The royalty must be apportioned between the patent and the trade mark, but since the value of the patent decreases, and that of the trade mark increases, with time, the agreement may make provision for varying the apportionment over a period of time.

Right to dispute validity of patent

As a result of a recent case[1] it is no longer lawful to prevent a licensee from contesting the validity of the licensed patent. This has caused considerable perturbation among lawyers, partly because it reversed an old common law doctrine at a stroke. The practical effect it may have on licensing practice is not immediately obvious, but informed opinion holds that the effect will be significant.

Exclusivity

This matter, though important, has been left to the last, since it is still only a gleam in the eye of the Department of Justice — caused by a report of a President's Task Force on Anti-

Trust Policy. At all events exclusive licences are still lawful and we are assured that there is no plan to challenge them. On the other hand, the agreement must include a right for the exclusive licensee to grant sub-licences, on the principle that at least one of the parties must be able to grant further licences. By the same token, an undertaking by a licensor to grant only one non-exclusive (sole) licence, or not to grant further licences (partial exclusivity), is generally not lawful unless, presumably, the licensee(s) has the right to grant sub-licences.

COLLABORATION CAUSING DIMINUTION OF COMPETITION

In the context of licensing, the main form of collaboration is that of research and development. Agreements providing for such collaboration were discussed in Chapter 4. As well as forming the main substance of an agreement it can also be part of a licensing "partnership" situation, also discussed in Chapter 4.

As a general rule, any agreement which provides for a continuing exchange of research information between companies that would otherwise be in competition is nowadays suspect, unless it is closely circumscribed to achieve some definite object where beneficial results are thought to outweigh the disadvantage of loss of competition. Any such legitimate agreement is likely to be limited to a short duration and to a closely defined technological field. An example might be an agreement enabling a potential licensee to assess an innovation before negotiating a licence agreement.

UNPATENTED KNOW-HOW

The third of the objectives of anti-trust formulated at the beginning of this chapter was to prevent encroachment of the patent monopoly concept on other creations of the mind. For the present purpose such creations may be confined to "know-how" as defined earlier in this book, remembering that the definition is restricted to confidential or secret information.

Attention has been drawn in various parts of this book to the difficulties inherent in treating know-how as a legal entity with attributes of negotiable property, and it has been pointed out that the law in the UK is still in a state of development. The same can be said of the USA with the added point that while patent monopolies must be tolerated because they are expressly provided for in the Constitution, no such privilege was or should be extended to unpatented know-how. This attitude was given judicial expression in Lear *v* Adkins[1] which cast considerable doubt on the legitimacy of "licensing" know-how. No definite judgement on the point was given, however, the federal Supreme Court leaving it to the State courts to rule. (Although patents are a federal matter, rights in respect of know-how are primarily within State jurisdiction.)

The Lear *v* Adkins judgement was nevertheless widely regarded as forecasting the shape of things to come and practitioners wondered whether it would any longer be lawful to make an agreement for disclosure of know-how in return for payment. This, bearing in mind that no one can be compelled to disclose what is in his mind unless he wants to, would be a *reductio ad absurdum* on any view of the matter, since it would effectively inhibit any such disclosure and hence close this avenue for usefully exploiting the know-how.

Only less authoritative than the federal Supreme Court in such matters is the Anti-trust Division of the Department of Justice, and a pronouncement by Mr R W McLaren,[2] head of that Division, should, it is thought, lay to rest the doubt raised (but not resolved) in Lear *v* Adkins. In effect Mr McLaren affirmed the legality of know-how licensing provided the know-how is "substantially secret" and that it is valuable. The latter, of course, follows from the premise that a licensee is offering money for it. Mr McLaren emphasised, however, that the provisions in anti-trust law applicable to patent licences must apply with at least equal force, *mutatis mutandis* to know-how.

Patent invalid or not yet granted

A special case of unpatented know-how is the subject matter of a patent application which is still pending. Before grant of the patent, this subject matter is unpatented but may well be secret. If it is secret, it can be the subject of a know-how licence until such time as the patent is granted. In any event, whether the subject matter is secret or not, the applicant for the patent can enter into an agreement whereby he promises that when and if a patent is issued, a licence will be granted to the other party to the agreement on specified terms. This, as pointed out in Chapter 4, is a valuable promise for which the licensee may be (and usually is) prepared to pay consideration. The amount and form of the consideration (whether a lump sum or a royalty on production) which may lawfully be agreed between the parties are matters which will no doubt be hotly disputed over the coming years. The difficulty has arisen because the dicta in Lear *v* Adkins lead to the presumption that in future the Courts will hold it unlawful to charge a royalty for a "licence" under a patent application.

If the author may give his personal opinion on this legally complex issue, it is that the judges in Lear *v* Adkins were landed in a semantic difficulty by the practice of referring to an agreement to grant a licence under a patent when (which necessarily includes "if") granted, as a "licence". Since no licence can in fact be granted unless there is a patent, the inference was drawn that the "licensor" (the applicant for the patent) had done something wrong in taking money ostensibly for a "licence." It is submitted that if the judges had recognised that the agreement was *in fact* an option for a licence, whatever words may have been used to describe it, they would have allowed that the optionor was entitled to get as much consideration, and in whatever form, as he could. After all, no prospective licensee is foolish enough to think that the grant of the patent would necessarily take place. If this analysis is correct, we may see attempts in future cases to compromise between the optionor's undoubted right to consideration on the one hand and deference to the judgement of Lear *v* Adkins on the other.

If a patent under which a licence has been granted is found invalid by the courts, it is likely, following the logic of Lear *v* Adkins, that, whatever the agreement says, the licensee can claim back any royalty he has paid. This is the other side of the ruling that the licensee is entitled to dispute the validity of the patent at any time during the licence. It seems to follow, though the point was not clearly made in Lear *v* Adkins, that if royalty has been paid under a pending patent application which does not mature to a granted patent or which results in a patent later found invalid, then that royalty payment also can be reclaimed by the licensee.

GENERAL ANTI-TRUST CONSIDERATIONS

Reference has been made more than once to "danger areas" and "suspect provisions." This phraseology has been used for two reasons: first, because of the severity of the sanctions against violation of the anti-trust law; second, because of the indeterminate extent of the law.

Sanctions

Violations can be dealt with under both civil and criminal law. The former operates with real "teeth" and orders can be made by the courts which completely upset a company's or group of companies' way of carrying on business, as well as making the patents involved unenforceable (on the ground of "misuse") not only against the other party to the agreement but against third parties. Damages can be heavy, being based on turnover rather than royalty values. If any element of restraint of trade is proved, triple damages may be awarded and this may bring the amount into the seven-figure bracket (in dollars).

Under criminal law, otherwise respectable businessmen may find themselves in gaol. This does not often happen, but the classic case was that a vice-president of the GE Company was sentenced to several months' imprisonment.

Whether sanctions can be enforced against non-American companies depends on whether they have assets or persons in the USA, including ownership of US patents or trade marks. Certainly a non-American company can be sued on the basis of a contract with an American company; the criterion is not the nationality of the company but whether what it has done has an effect on commerce within the USA, including export trade from that country.

Extent of anti-trust law

As already stated, anti-trust law is based on statutes which refer in the widest terms to monopolisation and restraint of trade. In applying them to licensing, it is said that the main purpose of the patentee must be lawful and if there is any resulting restraint of trade it must be merely ancillary to such main purpose.

Since the purpose of the patent system set out in the Constitution is "to promote the Progress of Science and Useful Arts" (PSUA), it is further said[3] that the patentee's main purpose, to be lawful, must be the same. This is where we run into a contradiction.

The system is based on the assumption that the best way to promote PSUA is to give the innovator a monopoly (a patent) so that his own interest is to maximise exploitation of the innovation. If reliance is to be placed on the patentee's self-interest, however, it cannot at the same time be placed on a motive attributed to the same patentee to promote PSUA, for these motives may on occasion conflict with each other. It is when and only when they do conflict that a potential violation of anti-trust law arises.

If it were a question of two wholly opposed motives leading to two opposite courses of action, then the patentee could, at least in theory, choose the "right" one of promoting PSUA, but this is far from being the case. The two motives in fact intermingle; there is no hard and fast line between them, and the possible courses of action are not wholly separate or clear-cut. In the author's opinion, therefore, the criterion of legality stated above can rarely if ever give the patentee a reliable guide to action in a concrete situation. What normally happens is that the patentee feels that his preferred way of exploiting his industrial property is the best way of promoting PSUA and he makes a judgement on how near he can get to it without infringing the law. This is necessarily a subjective judgement based on an assessment of the cases and experience of past situations.

These considerations are of a rather philosophical kind but they have their practical importance, which is this: whatever the logical validity of the above-stated criterion of legality, the intent of the parties to an agreement is a major factor in anti-trust actions, their intent being judged by what they have done and said. Since the court will inevitably accord to the adversary the right to inspect any relevant documents in the files of the parties to the agreement, it is of great practical importance for them to establish their good intentions in the internal and external correspondence leading up to the agreement. A good example of this is the withholding of licences under equivalent patents outside the USA. This in itself, as stated above, is lawful, but if the correspondence shows that the parties were seeking to set up a territorial market-sharing arrangement, then the withholding of licences under non-American patents would most likely be held to be a violation of the anti-trust law.

In sum, we would submit that while the intentions of the parties are of vital importance, if not governing, if an agreement comes into court, they can only measure their intentions by reference to the law; and that to make an actual determination of what the law is they can only study the decided cases and try to extract general rules from their particular facts.

This, it may be said, is the usual way of ascertaining the state of the law. This is true, but in the case of anti-trust, it is rendered exceptionally uncertain by the continuing change or development of the law, not slowly and in detail (such as may occur in any branch of the law) but rapidly and in major respects. The mechanism for this development depends on the role of the Department of Justice, which is charged with taking legal action against supposed anti-trust violation. If the Department considers, in its own discretion, that a given practice is suspect, it may bring an action in the courts against a company which has practised it. That company knows that such an action, if defended, will disrupt its business over a period of years and cost a large sum of money, and a good deal of embarrassment. The company, however, has the option of settling out of court, and is quite likely to do so. The resulting consent order is then promulgated by the court and becomes part of the case law. The net result is that the Department of Justice has established the illegality of that particular licensing practice.

The important point is that this acts retrospectively against any *existing* agreements which are on all fours with the one that was attacked. It follows that one or more provisions of an agreement which, on the basis of the only available criterion — the decided cases — was perfectly lawful when it was signed, may become unlawful during its life, on the basis of later decided cases. The effect of this and the heavy sanctions attaching to an illegal agreement is to make negotiators very wary of including provisions which *could* be frowned on by the Department in the future. This whole process has been confirmed and almost formalised by pronouncements from the Department about its future policy.[4] The above discussion will have made it clear that a statement that a given practice is on the Department's list is almost as good in its deterrent effect as a judgement by the Supreme Court. Moreover, the general effect of these interacting factors is to give anti-trust and the views of the Department a moral content which is in itself persuasive on judges, and makes it even less profitable for a company to defend an anti-trust action.

Effect on negotiations

The mode of development of anti-trust law has been described at length, both because of its inherent interest and because of its effect on negotiations, particularly between an American and a non-American company. The non-American often has an uneasy feeling that the American, with his greater knowledge of the subject, is invoking anti-trust for his own ends, to get an agreement more favourable to himself. While the uncertainty of the law and its heavy sanctions do favour this approach, the reader should in all fairness realise that the American negotiator is rightly looking beyond the law as it exists today to what it might become tomorrow, and on top of all the other commercial factors in the deal he has to decide whether his view of what the law may be or become, represents a reasonable commercial risk.

LEGAL RESTRAINTS IN THE UK

One man's restraint is another man's liberty. Freedom to enter into any kind of agreement may result in restraint of trade or competition. Complete freedom of trade and competition results in restraints on the kind of agreement which may be entered into. The fundamental difference between US anti-trust law and the corresponding provisions of the UK law is that in the USA freedom of trade and competition is regarded as the absolute and any agreement which could interfere with it has to be justified, whereas in the UK the right of anyone to run his own business (including the exploitation of any patent he may have) and enter into any contract he chooses is absolute and any restraint must be justified in terms of the common law doctrine of restraint of trade or a specific act of the legislature. (This, of course, refers to the practical operation of the law in relation to licensing, and not to any principles of philosophy, politics or economics.) Thus, while the combined operation of the Department of Justice and the legal apparatus in the USA derives inspiration from the *spirit* of the anti-trust law, the administration of the corresponding law in the UK tends to concentrate on the *letter*, as was made clear in the majority decision of the House of Lords in the case of Tool Metal Manufacturing Co *v* Tungsten Electric Co.[5]

In the UK, then, we have to consider the common law doctrine of restraint of trade and certain specific enactments of Parliament. The first can be dismissed very quickly by stating that, at least in practice, this doctrine has little or no applicability to licensing over and above that of the relevant statutes. It is worth noting in passing, however, that it does have a peripheral effect on the subject in its bearing on the provisions of employer/employee agreements concerning the relative rights of the parties in respect of technology learnt or originated by an employee or, more especially, an ex-employee. Any service agreement which is unduly restrictive in this respect must be held to be in restraint of trade and hence unenforceable.

The relevant statutes are the Monopolies Act 1948, Monopolies and Mergers Act 1965. Resale Prices Act 1964, and Restrictive Trade Practices Acts 1956 and 1968, in addition to certain sections of the Patents Act 1949.

MONOPOLIES AND RESTRICTIVE TRADE PRACTICES

By and large, the provisions of these Acts do not substantially affect industrial property licensing. In a general way, the Monopolies Acts and the Restrictive Trade Practices Acts divide the field into activities which result in a monopoly position on the one hand, and agreements between two or more parties having restrictions, such as price or territorial control, on the other. The former are dealt with by reference by the appropriate government department to the Monopolies Commission and the latter by registration of the relevant agreement by the Registrar of Restrictive Trading Agreements who in turn refers it to the Restrictive Practices Court. The criteria which determine whether an agreement falls within the Restrictive Trade Practices Acts are complex and technical, but agreements which fall outside the Acts may be dealt with by the Monopolies Commission if they form part of a monopoly position.

The powers of the Monopolies Commission are restricted to making recommendations to the government, which then seeks to persuade the companies concerned to remedy any practices found to be against the public interest. Such practices could involve, though they rarely have, dealings with patents. The ultimate sanction against a recalcitrant company is the issue, with the approval of Parliament, of a Statutory Order, but the Acts provide that such an Order cannot restrict the enforcement of a patent or the conditions of a patent licence. It will be appreciated that the practical effect of these provisions on the negotiation of licence agreements is minimal.

The need to register restrictive trade agreements under the Restrictive Trade Practices Acts has a considerable effect on agreements to which it applies, but patent, know-how and trade-mark licences (registered user agreements) are, in the main, specifically exempted. The effect of the Acts on licence agreements is accordingly limited to cases in which such an agreement contains also restrictions unrelated to the licence proper. The effect of the Acts (including the exact scope of the exemptions, which is a complex and technical matter) is, therefore, regarded as being outside the scope of this work.

Resale price maintenance was made unlawful by the Resale Prices Act 1964. Before this Act, it was legitimate to sell a patented product with a "limited licence" to resell it subject to price control, but such a practice is no longer permitted. It is, however, still legitimate to provide in an agreement in which the licensee is a manufacturer that the licensee shall sell at controlled prices, but this control cannot extend beyond the first sale.

ILLEGAL TYING CLAUSES

Section 57 of the Patents Act 1949 provides, *inter alia*, that any condition of a contract for the use of a patented article, or the working of a patented process, which requires the licensee to acquire from the licensor any unpatented article or material, shall be "void." This prohibition of tying clauses was discussed in Chapter 4 in connection with licensing policy for "user" inventions. It is the only legal restraint on licensing that has any real force behind it.

Any contract condition that is void under section 57 is unenforceable. More important, however, is the provision that so long as such a condition is in existence, it is a complete defence against an action for infringement of the patent. It thus has the effect of destroying the rights under the patent whether against the licensee or any third party.

There are, however, ways of avoiding partially the effect of the section, as mentioned in Chapter 4 — the principal one is set out in the Act itself. Section 57(2)(*a*) states that it is lawful to make a licence conditional on purchase of unpatented material, provided that the licensee has an option to purchase the material elsewhere "on reasonable terms specified in the contract." In practice this will normally mean a "reasonable" royalty, and it is thought that the fact that the licensee has accepted the royalty by signing the agreement containing the option is at least a *prima facie* basis for regarding it as reasonable. While this contrivance goes some of the way, it is obviously far from giving the patentee the guarantee he wants that the licensee must purchase from him.

Another way of legitimising a tying clause is to give the

licensee the right to terminate the liability on three months' notice, with provision (subject to arbitration) for compensating the licensor. This is not a method which normally appeals to businessmen.

It is also legitimate (*s*57(5)) for the licensor to reserve the right to supply articles for repair, and also to prevent the licensee from *selling* goods other than those supplied by the licensor.

As mentioned above, it is the letter rather than the spirit of *s*57 which counts. It is therefore possible to think of loopholes provided by the wording of the section. For example the contract that was held to be lawful in the Tool Metal case [5], referred to above, provided for a financial penalty if the licensee purchased the relevant material from a supplier other than the licensor. Since it appears from the judgement that the Lords believed the penalty to be commercially prohibitive, it follows that they were effectively legitimising the monopolisation (in a commercial sense) of supply by the licensor. That, however, was in 1941, and there is some doubt whether the courts would take such a lenient view today.

Another way of getting some of the benefit of a tying clause without infringing the section, which is put forward as a possibility without any authority behind it, is to provide in the agreement that the licensee shall purchase from the licensor, but that breach of this undertaking will *not* lead to termination of the licence. Thus the provision would not be a "condition" of the licence as laid down in *s*57. The patentee's remedy would lie only in an action for damages for breach of contract, but in practice this weapon would be quite persuasive.

Label licences

Yet another way round is the technique known as label licensing. Here the patentee includes, with every batch of the unpatented material which is sold, a statement on the label or invoice that purchase of that batch gives the purchaser a free licence under the relevant patent. This is thought to avoid the section, because by the time the licence has been granted, the purchase has already been made, so that the licence cannot be regarded as conditional on it. This arrangement, as indicated in Chapter 4, is legally viable so long as the purchaser does not require a promise of a *continuing* licence. Once this is given, section 57 is infringed.

RIGHT TO TERMINATE

Section 58 of the Patents Act enables either party to terminate an agreement "relating" to a licence under a patent when that patent expires, whatever the agreement says. The section is concerned with the expiry of a patent (or all the patents) which was in existence at the time when the contract was entered into and protects the product made under the licence. It follows that the addition of new patents (such as improvements) during the life of the contract does not act to extend the contract; if the parties want this they must make a new agreement under the new patent. To this extent the statement on page 102 to the effect that the addition of new patents would extend an agreement indefinitely needs to be qualified by excepting licences under UK patents.

If the parties want to negotiate an agreement involving know-how provisions as well as a patent licence which will continue in respect of the know-how after the patent has expired, they will not be able to do so unless they can completely sever the know-how and the patent provisions from each other. The difficulty about this is to make an allocation of royalty, when the agreement is negotiated, between the patent and know-how content of the licence. This, as explained in Chapter 2, is not as simple as it sounds.

LEGAL RESTRAINTS IN OTHER COUNTRIES

Restraints on licensing in countries other than USA and UK can be roughly classified into the following categories:

1 Restraints resembling US anti-trust laws. The main or only country in this category is Canada
2 Restraints broadly similar to those in the UK. In this group are most of the countries having a system of

restrictions, of which the following may be mentioned:
(a) Australia and New Zealand, which closely follow the British system
(b) The Common Market and Japan which differ from the UK in laying down a wider range of restraints and interpreting the relevant provisions of the law according to the spirit rather than the letter

3 Restraints designed to limit the penetration of technology under foreign control and the export of currency. These are to be found mainly in the developing countries, notably India and some South American countries

In the Scandinavian countries, restraints on the freedom to enter into licence agreements are limited to a "restraint of trade" type of provision which applies to contracts in general. It is a matter between the parties to the contract rather than one of public concern.

Canada

The situation here can be regarded in a general way as being the US anti-trust system called by a different name — the Combines Act — and having a noticeably British flavour. The main differences from the US law in practice arise from the following factors:

1 The Canadian statute makes a more detailed codification of the prohibited practices and this tends towards greater certainty of the law
2 A party aggrieved by a combine situation in Canada has no private remedy

This removes one of the greatest sanctions of the US law, namely the fear by the anti-trust violator that he may be liable in a civil action to extremely heavy damages, possibly on the triple scale. Action in Canada can be taken only by the Crown, but an aggrieved party does have the right to ask the Exchequer Court under the Combines Investigation Act (*s*30) to take action, such as setting aside the offending agreement, revoking a relevant patent or cancelling a trademark registration.

Less tangible but possibly more significant is the fact that the Canadian authorities show substantially less of the crusading spirit than do those of the USA in formulating their views on what should be regarded as unlawful practices, in ferreting out such practices and in sueing the parties concerned. Hence we do not see the rapid development of the law in Canada that has been taking place in the USA, but it should be remembered that the close economic association between the two countries inevitably leads to some influence of the US anti-trust law on Canadian practices and trends.

The Common Market countries

Although each of the six countries has its own domestic system of law governing restrictions on industrial property licensing, the system of law set up by the Treaty of Rome applies in the case of any agreement affecting trade between member countries. It is thought that UK and US readers are for the most part unlikely to be concerned as parties to agreements affecting trade only within one of the Common Market countries and, therefore, the detailed respects in which the domestic laws differ from each other and from Common Market law will not be discussed. It is true that the UK may soon become a member, and UK readers will always be concerned with agreements confined to their own country, but the UK law has already been discussed at some length.

The structure of the Common Market law, though not necessarily the philosophy behind it, bears some resemblance to the UK law on monopolies and restrictive practices. In a rough-and-ready way, *s*86 of the Treaty of Rome can be thought of as analogous to the Monopolies Act and *s*85 to the Restrictive Trade Practices Acts. Agreements which might offend against either section must be registered with the EEC Commission and will be adjudicated by the Commission. There is a right of appeal to the European Court of Justice.

The provisions of *ss*85 and 86 of the Treaty apply to any agreement having an effect on Common Market trade, regardless (at least in theory) of whether or not one or both of the parties is a national of a member country or where the agreement was made. The penalties for infringing the law can be very high, up to a million dollars for example, and this puts a heavy premium on registering a doubtful agreement for clearance by the Commission.

So far as licensing is concerned, the main unlawful practices fall into two groups:

1 Clauses in agreements which tie the licensee to a specified source of supply of unpatented materials, or which have the effect of continuing the agreement after the relevant patent has expired
2 Restrictions which affect export from one Common Market country to another

As regards the first group, the position is similar to that under *ss*57 and 58 of the UK Patents Act, except that the various methods of avoiding *s*57, such as giving the licensee an option to purchase the unpatented material otherwise than from the patentee but at a differential royalty rate, are not likely to be acceptable.

In this connection, and even more so in connection with the use of patents and trade marks to restrict trade between member countries, it should be borne in mind that *ss*85 and 86 resemble the US anti-trust statutes in being very generally worded, with the result that the true scope of the law will emerge only as a result of judicial application of the sections to particular cases. It is, at the time of writing, certain that an agreement granting a licence from *A* in country *X* to *B* in country *Y* which could limit the free flow of goods from *X* to *Y* is unlawful if it is not based on the possession of a patent by *A* in *Y*. The position if *A* does have a patent in *Y* is still in a state of evolution. It is true that in a recent case the Court of Justice held that the American owner *A* of a patent in Holland (*Y*) could use it to prevent importation of a product made in Italy (*X*) by an unrelated Italian company *B*. On the other hand, in this case, as it happened, there was no corresponding patent in Italy (*X*) and no connection between *A* and *B*; the outcome might have been different if there had been an Italian patent and *B* had manufactured in Italy (*X*) under a licence from *A*, the terms of which precluded export to Holland (*Y*) and again if *A* had been a national of a member country. It seems clear that the EEC Commission has an active policy in these matters which it is seeking to propagate both by case law and by supporting the negotiations for the setting up of a system for a Common Market patent.

The draft convention for the Common Market patent system explicitly provides that after a transitional period a Common Market patent should not be usable to prevent free flow of goods. It also provides that while national patent systems can initially coexist with the Common Market system, any possibility of using a national patent to restrict trade within the Common Market must be eliminated within the transitional period. This is given in the draft as five years but it appears that as a result of pressure by industrial interests this will be changed to ten years. In any event informed opinion holds that it may be ten years before the Common Market patent system comes into operation, in which case the transitional period will not end until 1990 at the earliest.

(The Common Market patent referred to here should not be confused with the "European Patent." This is a convention which is being negotiated by all the western European countries for setting up a European patent office which would grant a patent that would have effect in as many of the countries as the applicant designates. This would result in a "bundle" of national patents, each subject to the separate jurisdiction of its own country. It is likely that this Convention will be completed before negotiations for the Common Market are pressed to a conclusion. The Common Market patent system would then make use of the same European patent office as the European patent system.)

Similar principles apply to the use of trade-mark rights to impede the flow of goods between Common Market countries, and two recent trade-mark cases have strengthened the trend towards preventing the use of trade-mark rights in this way.

While there is still some uncertainty about the extent to which patent or trade-mark rights can be used to prevent a party to a licence agreement from exporting to another member country, any such doubt applies only to sale by the licensee himself. There is no doubt that once he has sold the patented or trade-marked product it can be resold anywhere in the EEC regardless of the licensor's patents or trade-mark registrations. The same principle applies to resale of a product originally sold by the patentee himself — he cannot use a patent or trade mark in any member country to prevent importation of that product. This is sometimes known as "exhaustion of patent or trade-mark rights" by the first sale of the product.

Japan

International licence agreements must be registered, within one month of their completion, with the Fair Trade Commission which is entitled to examine them and raise any objection under the Anti-Monopoly Act. Failure to register renders the agreement void. The main restrictions in licence agreements which are contrary to this Act are set out in a document, *Anti-Monopoly Act Guidelines for International Licensing Agreements*, dated 24 May 1968, issued by the Fair Trade Commission. The practices which are not permitted can be briefly summarised as restriction of the right to export (absolutely or in respect of price or quantity), except to countries where the licensor has a relevant patent or is already selling the goods; restrictions on dealing in competing goods; tying clauses (although a differential royalty rate is probably permissible); restrictions on resale prices; an obligation on the licensee to communicate know-how and assign rights in improvements to the licensor unless the licensor accepts a reciprocal obligation; the charging of royalties on goods which do not fall within the licensed patents or use the licensed technology.

It appears that the Commission does not automatically scrutinise registered agreements, but will do so if any complaint arises. Presumably the licensee could bring to the attention of the Commission any provision to which he wished to take exception.

For the sake of those familiar with the submission of agreements to MITI for vetting *before* completion, it should be noted that this requirement was abolished by the liberalisation measures of 1 June 1968.

India

While government control of the exploitation of technology and export of foreign currency by foreign licensors is being relaxed in Japan, in India it is being intensified. A new Patent Act has recently been passed which drastically reduces the rights of patentees to exploit their inventions. In view of the state of development of Indian research and inventiveness, this mostly means foreign patentees. The new Act gives the government rights which can be exercised by administrative action to revoke or operate under patents which are so extensive as virtually to destroy the patent monopoly.

In order that the spirit in which the Act is likely to be administered may be understood, it is worth describing its political origin. The Minister of Health decided that pharmaceutical patents were seriously impeding the development of medical services in India. Her proposed reforms generated the impetus for a reform of the patent system as a whole resulting in particularly severe restrictions on pharmaceutical patents, some of these restrictions being extended to chemical patents in general. The main points, apart from the government rights mentioned above which refer to all patents, are restriction of the term of a pharmaceutical patent to seven years (instead of sixteen, as in the UK) and the automatic licensing after three years from grant of all chemical patents (including pharmaceuticals) at a royalty not exceeding 4 per cent of the value of the patented bulk product made by the licensee. Since this value does not include the cost of research, formulation, packaging, distribution, promotion or technical service, the 4 per cent royalty can in most cases be regarded as only nominal. To understand this situation it is worth quoting the words of a Minister of the Indian government during the debate on the bill. He described it as "a big stick to bring to book black marketeers and racketeers in drugs who are playing havoc in the country." In fairness to the Indian government it should, however, be mentioned that many other countries, including the UK, have special provisions on pharmaceutical patents (see pages 135-6).

The Indian government also exercises control of licence

agreements with foreign licensors, whether relating to patents, know-how or trade marks, from the foreign exchange and fiscal points of view. For this purpose, proposed agreements must be submitted to the government for approval or otherwise. Securing a decision is likely to be a major operation. As a possible way round this, patentees may wish to try the route of endorsing the patents "licences of right" (see page 135), leaving it to the Comptroller of Patents to settle the terms of the licence, thus trading a government-approved licence for the right to choose one's licensees and decide the terms (a right already much curtailed, as indicated above, for chemical patents) and then run the gauntlet of securing foreign exchange approval from the government.

A point to notice is that, unlike most countries, in India registration of all licence agreements, which will then be open to public inspection, has been made compulsory (on registration, see pages 153-5).

South America

Restraints on licensing are due to come into force in 1971 in the Andean sub-regional Common Market (ANCOM) consisting of Bolivia, Chile, Columbia, Ecuador and Peru. The governing body of ANCOM has produced a code entitled *Common Rules Governing the Treatment of Foreign Capital, Trade Marks, Patents, Licences and Royalties.* The nature of the code can be sufficiently indicated for present purposes by stating that its objects are to exclude foreign investments from key sectors of the economy, to eliminate foreign control of companies and to diminish reliance on foreign technology.

The Rules combine features of the Indian control of licences granted by foreign licensors with provisions analogous to the European Common Market anti-trust law, with the difference that they are applied only to agreements with foreign licensors and not, apparently, to agreements within ANCOM. Thus, agreements with foreign licensors must be registered with the ANCOM control office by the end of 1971 and new agreements must be approved in advance. The sort of provision which will not be acceptable will by now be familiar to the reader, bearing in mind that the main motive is the protection of a particularly undeveloped region rather than the control of monopolistic or restrictive practices within the region.

A law has very recently been enacted in Argentina which is obviously motivated by considerations similar to those of ANCOM. It requires registration of all licence agreements, but refuses registration of those having certain provisions of the kind we can recognise as objectionable to developing countries. The net result is that such agreements will be invalid.

THE EFFECTS OF RESTRICTIVE LEGISLATION

Perhaps it would be appropriate as an epilogue to this consideration of restraints on licence agreements of what we might call the economic type operated by developing countries like India and the American countries, to point out that most restraints of this kind are equally likely to have the opposite effect to the one intended, since the person who might generate and license industrial property can always refrain from doing so if he does not like the terms available to him. The same remark applies, though with less force, to the "anti-trust" type of restraints more particularly associated with the advanced countries, with the USA to the fore.

Take the case of applicational research to discover new uses of a company's products with the commercial object of improving the market for such products. Clearly no company will be keen to spend money on research, the fruits of which will be equally available to competitors. It follows that a legal veto on tying a licence to purchase of the product from the originator of the new use, will be a factor *against* including this kind of research in the company's research programme — not necessarily the decisive factor but one which could tip the balance in a doubtful case.

COMPULSORY LICENCES

While legal restraints on licensing can act as a disincentive to research and development, the extent to which a patentee can inhibit licensing of a patent once granted is limited by the provisions in the law of nearly all countries against "abuse of monopoly." These provisions derogate from the monopoly granted to the patentee in a manner sanctioned by the International Convention (see Chapter 1) and hence more or less standardised throughout the industrial countries, with two exceptions — USA and Canada. Basically, the penalty for "abuse of monopoly" is the granting of a compulsory licence by the patent office concerned. It is this practice which does not exist in the North American countries. The reader will, however, have gathered that the absence of this particular penalty does not indicate any tolerance of abuse of monopoly in these countries — on the contrary it is treated considerably more severely there than in the rest of the world but using different legal forms and sanctions.

Abuse of monopoly is held to have occurred if the patentee has failed to satisfy a demand for the patented product either by not manufacturing at all or by taking advantage of his monopoly position to place the product on the market on impossible terms. It is a significant symptom of the nationalistic nature of patent systems that a patentee is not regarded as having discharged his obligation to "work" his invention if he has merely imported the product of the invention manufactured abroad.

Another practice which ranks as abuse of monopoly is to prevent a later patentee from operating his own patented invention. It will be remembered that this can take place if the later patentee's (*B*'s) invention falls within the fenced-off area of a patent belonging to an earlier inventor *A*. In order to be able to work his own invention, *B* has to obtain a licence from *A*. If the latter refuses to grant such a licence, he is guilty of abuse of monopoly, because he is holding up development of the very act which the grant of a patent to *B* was intended to foster.

Compulsory licences in the UK

If a person wishes to operate a patented invention and is unable to obtain a licence from the patentee, and believes he can make out a case that the patentee is abusing his monopoly in one of the special senses described above, he can apply to the Patent Office for a compulsory licence, but only if three years from the *grant* of the patent have elapsed. The Patent Office takes evidence regarding the alleged abuse of monopoly and the competence of the applicant for a licence to operate the invention, and decides whether to grant the licence and on what terms. This is a rather elaborate procedure (at least in the UK) and is likely to take at least two or three years and a good deal of effort. For this reason the procedure is seldom invoked, but it would be a mistake to assume from this that the compulsory licence provisions are ineffective. They stand in the background as a deterrent to a dog-in-the-manger patentee, and a threat to use them by a person desiring a licence may bring an offer hitherto adamantly refused.

It may be noted, in passing, that the existence of these provisions accounts for the total scepticism with which those concerned with patents regard accusations that a patent has been used to "suppress" this or that invention.

Licences of right

A patentee can save himself half his annual renewal fees if he endorses his patent, "licences of right." This means that the patentee has to grant a licence to anyone who asks for one, the Patent Office settling the terms if the parties cannot reach agreement. To the uninitiated, this is sometimes regarded as a way of finding licensees if one wishes to exploit a patent by licensing. In practice this is not so, and the endorsement, "licences of right," usually means that the patentee has almost given up hope of making good use of the patent but cannot quite bring himself to allow it to lapse altogether. He therefore compromises on a strictly 50 per cent basis.

Food and medicine

Many countries, notably the UK, provide for the granting of compulsory licences under patents relating to food or medicine to any competent applicant, even if there has been no abuse of monopoly. Unlike applications under the abuse of monopoly provisions, these licences can be applied for immediately the patent is granted. There have been several successful applications for licences under pharmaceutical patents in the last ten years or so, and since this may have a significant effect on private negotiations, it may represent only the tip of an iceberg which is of considerable importance to the pharmaceutical industry.

COMMUNIST COUNTRIES

The reader may wonder what application the principles discussed in this chapter has to the countries in which the economy is wholly or substantially in the hands of the state — that is a "socialist" economy in the strict sense of the word. If we confine ourselves to countries in which licensing is significant, this means USSR and the eastern European countries.

It should be noted first of all that the concept of industrial property rights is something of an anomaly in a socialist economy, since it is designed to enable an originating company to monopolise its innovations as against competitors. The appropriate reward for innovators under socialism is not a monopoly but a straight payment by the state to the individual concerned. This is, in fact, the Russian system known as the "author's certificate." In parallel with this, the USSR has always operated a patent system of sorts, but about ten or fifteen years ago it decided to launch a fully fledged western-type system and join the International Convention. It may be surmised that the intention behind this was to enable the USSR to obtain patents in capitalist countries and exploit them in those countries by licensing.

The other side of this coin is the facility for companies in capitalist states to obtain patents in the USSR, and after a rather hesitating start the Russian Patent Office appears to have settled down to an intelligible patent-granting procedure. The value of such patents is problematical. Certainly the USSR is willing, and sometimes keen, to purchase technology, but this is only likely to apply to major projects such as the building of a plant to make a chemical product or the installation of a computer-controlled process. What is the relative importance of the know-how and any relevant patents in such a deal? The importance of the know-how is self-evident. The relevance of the patents is determined primarily by the extent to which they could, in the absence of an agreement, be enforced against the Russian state. It is submitted that this is not a real possibility in terms of practical politics, but if this is not enough, there is an explicit provision in the Russian Patents Act (*s*5.48*(g)*) that the USSR can make use of a patented invention if it is of "special importance to the state," importance being established by the government.

There is, however, another aspect to the use of Russian patents: the extent to which they affect the choice of licensor if two or more non-Russian companies are competing to grant a Russian licence. The best opinion is that in such a case the USSR plays the patent game by western rules and favours the company holding the patent or patents that control the technology.

The handling of licences and licence negotiations is itself a state monopoly and an organisation called Licensintorg has been set up for this purpose and is now a going concern. The route to Licensintorg may, however, be the State Committee of Science and Technology, which, in consultation with the relevant Ministry decides whether a licence is in principle desirable. A difficulty in agreeing the monetary consideration for a licence is the reluctance of the authorities to disclose the extent of their production. This usually dictates a lump-sum payment rather than a royalty. The prevailing opinion is that while Licensintorg strikes a hard bargain and takes an inordinately long time doing it, once the agreement has been signed it is scrupulously observed by the Russian side.

Similar considerations apply to the eastern European countries, although it will be found that patent and licensing matters are on the whole processed with greater facility owing to the existence of a residue of professional experience from pre-war days.

If the role of patents in Communist countries is doubtful, that of registered trade marks is even more so, since promotion in the capitalist sense hardly exists at all. It is perhaps possible, however, to envisage a case where the registration of a well-known name for a product or process which the Russians would want to use for their own designation, could be a favourable factor for the trade-mark owner as against capitalist competitors for the deal.

NOTES AND REFERENCES

1 Lear *v* Adkins, 395 US 693 (1969)

2 Address to Symposium on Patent Law, 25-6 September 1969, reprinted in *Current Anti-Trust Problems in Acquiring and Licensing Patents, Trade Marks and Technology*, published by the Practising Law Institute, 1969, pages 5-10

3 See, for example, van Cise, "Anti-trust laws and patents," *Journal of the Patent Office Society*, volume 52, 1970, page 776

4 See, for example, R. W. McLaren, Address to PTC Research Institute, 5 June 1969, reprinted in *Current Anti-trust Problems in Acquiring and Licensing Patents, Trade Marks and Technology*, published by the Practising Law Institute, 1969, pages 87-105

5 *Reports of Patent Cases*, volume 58, 1941, page 209.

Chapter 6

The wording of licence agreements

This chapter marches on the boundary between the businessman's conception of the deal he would like to make and the professional craftsman's work of creating the verbal structure to embody it. Chapter 2 discussed at some length the differing functions and outlook of businessmen and lawyers in relation to contracts. The principle was stated that the wording of the contract should be that which expresses the intentions of the businessmen who negotiated the agreement, but this principle is not as simple as it sounds. The ultimate purpose of a contract is in fact to express the agreement between the parties in a form in which it can be enforced by a court of law, probably years after the agreement was made. The vital point is that the arbiter of the meaning of the words is a judge, who is drawn from the ranks of the legal profession. Now the frame of mind of a man with legal training and who is considering the matter in the context of a legal dispute is inherently very different from that of the businessman negotiating the agreement years ago. Not only are the mental training and experience of the two men different in kind, but the specific facts of the case itself as they are known to the judge today on the one hand, and to the businessman when the agreement was made years ago on the other, are also very different. Moreover it is to some extent a myth to suppose that the two businessmen were themselves completely of one mind when they signed the agreement. The wording is intended to express such an identity of view, but in practice it all too often covers tacit differences which may be at the very centre of the dispute. The capacity of even the most brilliant judge to bridge all these gaps is strictly limited.

However, some of the bridging work will have been done in advance if the contract was written by a lawyer. He can discuss intimately with his businessman/client the latter's intentions at the time the contract is negotiated and can reconcile them with the other party's intentions through his lawyer. If this job was done properly, the judge in any dispute starts off with a clear statement of the businessmen's intentions so far as this can be understood by and written down in the language of the lawyer. Thus, it is not because businessmen's language is not more *appropriate* to express businessmen's intentions that contracts are written in legal language; on the contrary, it is because the eventual arbiter of the contract is not a businessman but a lawyer.

Against this, however, is the fact that relatively few contracts do in fact reach the courts, so that in the great majority of cases the businessmen are saddled with an unfamiliar mode of expressing their intentions all to no purpose. Nevertheless, the discipline of legal drafting is by no means wasted. If the negotiators always arrived at an unambiguous bargain and took the trouble to express this in clear language, there would be no problem. In fact businessmen, as was explained in Chapter 2, seldom do either of these things if left to themselves, and it is the job of the lawyers to make them. Hence the work of the lawyers kills three birds with one stone: it ensures that the negotiators really have made an agreement, that the latter is expressed in unambiguous language and that that language is the one spoken by the final arbiter in the unlikely event that matters ever reach that stage; and if the skill of the draftsman never comes to be tested in court, this may be precisely because that skill had been well and truly applied.

The fact remains that the dialogue between the lawyer and the businessman necessary to achieve a satisfactory form of words is not always an easy one. While the craftsman must be left free to carry out his client's design, the client has a much better chance of getting what he wants if he understands something about the material in which the craftsman works — in this case the words in which the contract is expressed. With this end in view, a few particular points of wording that arise in licence agreements will be discussed. At the same time licence terms that were not dealt with in Chapter 4 will be considered.

It will be noted that the term "wording" is used rather than the more natural "language." This is to ensure that the theme is not confused with that of the choice of language for an agreement between parties speaking different languages such as English and German.

No attempt will be made to provide standard forms of words for use in agreements. There are a number of books of so-called "precedents" which fulfil this object and it is thought that they are more suitable for use by the practitioner than the businessman.

GENERAL PRINCIPLES

As shown above, the object of a contract is to enable one party *A* to hold the other *B* to a promise or undertaking *B* has given in return for something which *A* has given or promised to *B*, and vice versa. The difficulty is to know exactly what the promises are. Consider, for instance, a promise by licensee *B* to pay licensor *A* a royalty of 5 per cent of the selling price of goods made under the licence. The price actually received by *B* for the goods will probably include items additional to *B*'s list price (based on cost plus profit) — for example, freight, packaging and tax. It may also have had deducted from it a discount for prompt payment, for bulk purchase and so on. When *B* works out the royalty he says the selling price is the sum actually received for the goods themselves — that is, not including the packaging and so on — and this will be the list price less any discounts. *A*, on the other hand, says the selling price is the figure given on the invoice but without allowing special favours to special customers — that is to say, the list price plus any additions, such as packaging, but without deducting discounts. Which one is right? In a simple situation a judge would probably plump for the list price as expressing the true value of the goods, a result which would also have the advantage of effecting a compromise between the parties; but it would cost the parties thousands of pounds, much effort and considerable unpleasantness to arrive at this decision.

In order to avoid a dispute of this nature, the parties ought to have defined the basis for the royalty with greater precision. In other words the dispute should have been resolved over the negotiating table before the agreement was signed. Once this has been done, there are various techniques of wording for expressing the agreement arrived at. For instance an explicit definition could be given of the term "selling price" (an agreement can always serve as its own dictionary) or a special term such as "net sales value," again with its own definition, could have been used. (This latter would have the advantage of emphasising that a special meaning was being given to the concept of price.) Whatever the method, it would involve some extra wording and elaboration of the agreement.

HOW MUCH ELABORATION?

The question now arises: how much elaboration must be endured? It might be thought that a definition of "selling price" as being the price charged to an arm's-length customer without including the additions or subtracting the discounts mentioned above would be enough. But the price charged depends on certain arbitrary factors such as the allocation of overheads between various products, so one could go on to elaborate the definition in terms of the accounting procedures used to arrive at the list price. It will be seen what vistas this opens up, and reference to Chapter 4 will show that the matter of selling price is not unique in this respect. The fact is that if all the possible circumstances which may arise in the life of an agreement were analysed and catered for in the wording of the document, it would be of inordinate length and complexity.

Clearly a judgement must be made in any particular case on how much to put in and how much to leave out. The judgement will be based on the experience of the negotiators and their lawyers in the light of a number of factors. Generally, the weightier the transaction the greater the degree of elaboration which is justified. On the other hand, elaboration takes time, which may mean a significant delay in getting the agreement signed and the project started. This illustrates one of the main difficulties in tackling the job. It is the lawyer who is most aware of the dangers of an insufficiently detailed document, and all his training leads him to stress the importance of this while tending to ignore the disadvantages in terms of delay, expense and effort. The businessman, on the other hand, prefers the simplest possible document and is usually in a hurry. Another factor is the legal system of the country concerned. In some countries, such as Germany, Switzerland and others in continental Europe, the courts are ready to imply various terms as being normal in a contract unless specifically excluded. A good illustration (though not necessarily a true one) would be an assumption that "selling price" had the particular meaning given to it above, unless the agreement gave a different definition. In English and American law, on the other hand, the general principle is that the courts will not infer anything which is not stated or implied by *the actual wording of the agreement*, although it must be emphasised that this is not pressed to extremes.

A good example of how these factors can work out in practice was a proposed licence agreement between a German and a British company with which the writer was concerned. The Germans submitted a draft four pages long. This was considered by a British solicitor who produced a new draft fourteen pages long having a great deal of elaboration including the following draftsman's gem:

> No waiver by either party of any of the provisions of this Agreement shall be deemed to have been made unless expressed in writing and signed by the party effecting such waiver and the failure of either party on any occasion to insist on strict performance of the terms, conditions and provisions of this agreement shall not act as a waiver of future compliance therewith nor shall the receipt by either party of any offer due from the other under this Agreement with knowledge of a breach by the other party of any of its obligations hereunder act as a waiver of such breach.

This kind of thing left the German company somewhat aghast and they simply picked up certain points in the new draft on which their original draft had been obviously inadequate and produced an amended version of that draft, still only five pages long. The negotiations ceased at that point for a technological reason but it was clear that the British negotiators had more sympathy with the German style than with that of their own lawyer, and that if a document had finally been agreed it would have been nearer the German than the British form.

POINTS OF DISPUTE

The settlement of differences which arise in negotiating the wording of an agreement is determined by the fact that, in spite of the protestations to the contrary, each of the negotiators is bent on having his own way. It is common to distinguish between drafting points and points of substance. These categories are convenient for the negotiator, who is normally a businessman or manager, since it enables him to wash his hands of points whose commercial importance does not seem to warrant the effort necessary to grasp their legal significance. Some examples were given in Chapter 4, and the way they are often handled in negotiations is mentioned in Chapter 8. On the other hand, the distinction is not really valid, since there is no "drafting point" which is worth considering at all that is not a point of substance. The document must be considered as a unity with every part of it having an effect on the relationship between the parties.

An example will illustrate the misleading possibilities of this classification into drafting points and points of substance. In a draft agreement prepared by *A* providing for the evaluation by *A* of certain samples furnished by *B*, it was stated that: "*A* may communicate to *B* all the information acquired by *A* in evaluating the samples." *B* altered "may" to "shall," thinking that this was a mere drafting mistake. *A*, however, refused to accept the alteration. There were many other points of difference and the negotiations continued for many months, but throughout this time *A* refused to make the firm commitment to reveal to *B* the results of the evaluation, which would have been involved in changing "may" to "shall." It is significant that the negotiations eventually fell through.

THE FORM OF A CONTRACT

In Chapter 2 it was mentioned that there is no necessary form for a contract. Two forms are in fact common in business life, the letter of agreement and the formal "legal" document. The first sets out the terms of the agreement in the form of a letter from *A* to *B* which is sent in duplicate with an invitation to *B* to countersign and return one copy, so as to signify that he "accepts the terms of this letter" or words to that effect. This completes the contract.

More usual, at least for licensing, is the formal document. This has four parts: the first sets out the date on which the agreement was made and the names and addresses of the parties; the second, called the "recitals", outlines the situation on which the contract is based; the third gives the terms of the agreement itself; the fourth provides for sealing or signature by the parties. The recitals always begin with the word "Whereas" which is something of a hallmark of legal drafting. Archaicisms of this kind do not come naturally to the businessmen whose intentions the agreement is intended to express, but they are accepted as giving an aura of professionalism to the job. On the other hand any archaicism that makes the document more difficult to understand than it need be ought to be resisted. Perhaps the chief of these is the absence of punctuation. The author is aware of explanations given by the apologists of this practice, but finds them unconvincing.

RECITALS AND DEFINITIONS

In the case of a simple patent licence, the recitals merely state that *A* is the owner of patents [traditionally, "letters patent"] numbers so-and-so and wishes to grant a licence to *B*, and *B* wishes to accept such a licence. In other words the recitals are only a formality. In such a case the technological field of the agreement is predetermined by the claims of the relevant patent(s). If, however, the agreement involves know-how on future patents, there is no ready-made definition of the field. The traditional way of setting up such a definition is to include a "Recital" on the following lines:

> "Whereas *A* is the owner of a process (hereinafter called the "Process") for making *X* [or whatever] which incorporates inventions described in the specification(s) of letters patent numbers ..."

If the reader recalls the nature of a patent, which involves a fenced-off area of technology, he will realise that this sort of definition does not work. Even if there is only one patent, the area it covers includes a large number, often an infinity, of processes. Moreover the description in the patent specification is worded at varying levels of generality. That is to say, parts of the specification delineate the fenced-off area as a whole, other parts refer to particular items within the total area, and there is a descriptive part giving detailed examples or drawings. Which of all these is meant by the phrase "described in the patent specification"? If there is more than one patent, the difficulty is compounded.

On the whole it is better, in any except the simplest agreements, to regard the recitals as a mere formality, and to have a separate "definitions" clause in which due attention can be paid to what is one of the most important and often one of the most difficult parts of the agreement to draft. First and foremost in this clause will be definitions of the technological field and the geographical territory of the agreement. Other items would normally be a definition of "patents" as meaning, for instance, the existing scheduled patents and patent applications and any later patents for improvements; a definition of improvements; of royalty-bearing products (not necessarily products within the technological field of the agreement); of the duration of the agreement; and of selling price, net selling price or net sales value, whichever term is selected.

Field of agreement and improvements

The definition of the field was discussed at some length in Chapter 4. Framing this definition is an exercise in drawing a verbal line or "fence" round an area of technology. The object is to define in advance what new know-how and inventions are to be brought into the agreement during its life. It may be that in a particular case, for example, if there is a dominant or "master" patent, the field is exactly the same as that covered by the broadest claim of this patent. If so the agreement should say so and not leave it as a matter of inference. Equally the agreement should not use the word "improvements" without an explicit definition of this term. It is a common mistake to suppose that it necessarily means something falling within the scope of the relevant patent (or one of them). What is really wanted is an explicit statement that an improvement means an invention falling within the field of the agreement. This can be visualised as a smaller fenced-off area falling within the fence which forms the boundary of the field.

Even this method can lead to difficulties. Thus, it can happen that a patent arising within the life of the agreement may overlap the field, being partly within it and partly without. Such a case might arise, for example, if the field is defined as brakes for road vehicles and a brake is invented which is applicable to railway vehicles as well. To deal with this possibility adds further complexity to the drafting, and is an example of the need to decide where to draw the line in any particular case between undue elaboration and risking possible areas of future disagreement.

Know-how and secrecy provisions

A possible definition of "know-how" is "Any confidential information within the field of the agreement which is in or comes into the possession of the licensor and which he is free to disclose to the licensee" (that is, he has not received it in confidence from someone else). The agreement should provide that the party receiving the know-how must keep it secret for a specified time — normally the life of the agreement but in some cases a lesser number of years. There is usually, however, a proviso that the recipient is released from secrecy if the know-how comes into the "public domain" (but not through his own fault), or was already in his possession or is received not in confidence from a third party.

THE LICENCE

Two points call for comment. Following the archaic wording of the official grant of a patent, the phrase, "a licence to make, use, exercise and vend" products (or whatever) falling within the patent(s), or utilising the know-how, is often used. The word "vend" is a straight synonym for "sell", but no one seems quite sure what "exercise" means if not the completely comprehensive "make, use or sell". On the principle of avoiding words of uncertain meaning, it is accordingly best to omit the word "exercise". Of course, a given agreement does not necessarily include all of the other words either. As described above, different rights may well be given in different countries — for example, the right to make in the UK and to sell in any country.

The second point arises if the relevant patent has not yet been granted. If the agreement says that a licence is granted under Patent Application number so-and-so, there is really no doubt what is meant, but to be strictly accurate it should say that the licensor will grant and the licensee will accept a licence under the patent when granted, and that meanwhile the terms and conditions of the agreement (where applicable) will apply as if a patent had been granted. This really amounts to an option agreement and the consideration for the option need not necessarily be (though it usually is) the same as for the eventual licence.

Sub-licences

If it is intended that the licensee shall have the right to grant sub-licences, the clause which gives the licensee a licence to make, use and/or sell (as the case may be) under the patent should add "and the right to grant sub-licences to others." This right may itself be limited to a special class of people (such as associated or subsidiary companies), or a special type of activity — for example, to use the patented products (but not to make or sell them). In the case of a "user" patent involving use of an unpatented material sold by the licensee, the licensor will often wish to limit the right to sub-license to the licensee's customers. This could fall foul of the prohibition on "tying clauses", and it is thought that approximately the same result could be obtained in many cases without the legal objection by a restriction which prevents the licensee from granting sub-licences to manufacturers of the relevant unpatented material — in other words, to the licensor's competitors.

ASSIGNMENT OF AGREEMENT

The agreement usually states that the licensee cannot assign the agreement to anyone else. The licensor is, however, sometimes willing to let the licensee assign to an associated or subsidiary company, though this might well be limited to those existing at the date of the agreement. As to the reverse situation, where the licensee is taken over by another company, the agreement usually provides that it shall terminate in such an event.

Restrictions of this kind are not normally placed on the licensor unless there is a strong element of reciprocity of the "partnership" variety described in Chapter 4.

ROYALTY

Enough has already been said in various parts of this book on the ins and outs of royalty provisions. The only further point to mention is that care should be taken in drafting an "annual minimum royalty" clause. This again is a phrase that everyone understands, but it can and should be more accurately expressed as an obligation to pay the difference between the actual royalty occurring in a given period (a year in this case) and a stated fixed sum.

Accounts and payment

The agreement should set out the requirement that the licensee furnish a statement of royalties, usually at dates separated by a six-monthly interval, and to pay the sum due within, say, one month of each such date, in a stated currency. The agreement usually gives the licensor the right to inspect the relevant books and records of the licensee either through the licensor's own accountant or an independent accountant agreed by both parties. While this provision is almost universal, it appears that it is seldom invoked; the mere existence of the provision is normally a sufficient safeguard.

If the deal involves payments both ways (for example, by virtue of cross-licences) one of the parties should be given the job of computing the balance due at the relevant payment dates, and paying it or invoicing the other party as the case may be.

PATENT COSTS

It is normally in the licensor's interest to prosecute his patent applications and pay the annual renewal fees which are necessary to keep his patents in force, but in the case of an exclusive licence the licensee may be prepared to accept this responsibility. The responsible party should, however, try to retain some discretion about which applications and patents to maintain at any time, since inventions can become obsolete, and the prosecution of a patent application to the bitter end may mean expensive actions in appeal courts in various countries. A compromise which is commonly accepted is to provide that the responsible party shall give the other one notice of any intention *not* to pay a fee, or take a prosecution action, in reasonable time before it becomes due, whereupon the other party can call for an assignment to him of the relevant patent or application and then proceed with it at his own cost.

Similar principles can be applied to the situation arising with an agreement involving improvement inventions when a party making an improvement invention has to consider in which countries to file patent applications. It can be provided that he notifies the other party in good time of his intentions, whereupon the latter has the option of filing an application in his own name and expense in any country not selected by the inventing party.

GRANT OF LICENCES TO THIRD PARTIES

Chapter 4 discussed the implications of dealing with a third party who infringes a licensed patent. It can be taken for granted that the most likely outcome in practice is for the licensor to offer the infringer a licence, and the original licensee's main concern therefore should be to ensure that such a licence is on terms not more favourable than his own. This "most-favoured licensee" (sometimes oddly called "most-favoured nation") clause can also be included as a general provision in any non-exclusive licence. It is one of the clauses that sounds simple enough but is in fact very difficult to draft with precision. This is because the later granted licence may, and in general will, contain various terms which cannot be quantified and no valid comparison can be made between the totality of the terms of the original licence and those of the later granted one. Probably the best compromise is to limit the clause to the *financial* terms of the two agreements; at least these can be compared even if a disadvantage in financial terms could in some cases be more than counterbalanced by some other advantage accorded to one of the licensees, and possibly not even stated in the agreement.

ARBITRATION

Provision can be made for arbitration of disputes under the whole agreement or certain specified clauses. It is probably worth providing for arbitration in respect of clauses involving a high content of technical facts, such as performance guarantees by the licensor. Otherwise it may well be that the parties could obtain better and not more expensive justice by taking the dispute to the courts.

The agreement can provide that the arbitrator will be a recognised authority such as the president of the relevant professional institute. Alternatively the agreement can provide for the parties to appoint an arbitrator, leaving it to the president of an institute to appoint someone if the parties cannot agree. It is convenient in agreements involving other countries to state that arbitration shall be in accordance with the rules of the International Chamber of Commerce, which provide a procedure for conciliation to precede arbitration. Doubts are sometimes expressed by US companies or their lawyers about the propriety of arbitration of disputes in connection with US patents, presumably on the ground that patent rights involve matters of public policy. These doubts are believed to be without foundation, except perhaps that arbitration would not be acceptable as a final determination of an anti-trust issue. As an alternative to the International Chamber of Commerce, American parties may prefer to use the American Arbitration Association.

COMMUNICATION

The agreement usually provides for any notice under the agreement to be sent by post and to be deemed to have been given at the date it should reach its destination in the ordinary course of post — an example of a provision which it hardly seems necessary to spell out.

WHICH COUNTRY'S LAW?

There are two aspects to the matter of jurisdiction when an agreement involves more than one country. The first is that of "venue" — that is, the country in which the plaintiff should take action for breach of the agreement. Normally the plaintiff will take action in the defendant's country, since he will want the court hearing the action to be able to make an enforceable order against the defendant.

The other matter is that of the law to be applied to the agreement and any dispute under it. At least in theory this is independent of venue, since if a court in one country decides that the applicable law in the case in question is that of another country, it will endeavour to apply that law with the help of expert evidence from the other country's lawyers.

What, then, is the applicable law? Sometimes it is written in the agreement that the law shall be that of a stated country — for example, English law or Swiss law or that of one of the states of the USA. However the wishes of the parties (as expressed in the agreement) do not necessarily bind the court, although they would no doubt tip the balance in a doubtful case. For example if an English licensor is granting licences to a German company under the licensor's German patents, a German court hearing an action brought against the licensee would presumably regard the contract as coming under German law even if the parties had agreed that the contract should be governed by English law.

The language to be used for the agreement is for the parties to decide, but the parties can, if they wish, provide for an agreed translation to be made, each version being then equally authentic.

EXCLUSION OF UNLAWFUL PROVISIONS

Enough has been said elsewhere in this book about unlawful provisions such as tying clauses. There is, however, one last resort which may be adopted if the parties find it necessary to include a provision which is of doubtful legality or which is lawful in one country but not in another. In such a case they may include a qualification to the doubtful provision on the following lines: "In so far as it is lawful ..." or, "In so far as it is lawful in any country of the territory of the agreement, ..." However, this expedient may not avail in countries such as the USA where the *intentions* of the parties are paramount.

REGISTRATION AND STAMPING

A patent licence can be entered on the Register of Patents by the licensee or licensor acting unilaterally. It is in fact in the licensee's rather than the licensor's interest to register, since registration protects the licensee against the licensor's doing a deal with a third party in contravention of the licence. For instance if the licence is exclusive and has not been registered, and the patentee grants a further licence, the original licensee's only remedy is to sue the patentee for damages; he cannot have the second licence annulled.

In the case of trade-mark licences, the parties can and should apply (in this case they must do it jointly) to have the licensee registered as a "registered user".

The licence deed to be registered must be submitted to the Patent Office and will be open to public inspection. It is common practice to make this deed a merely formal document and to set out the commercial terms on which the licence is based in a separate agreement. The Patent Office will require to see this for checking purposes, but it will not be open to inspection.

It is often remarked by those interested in, but not familiar with, the working of the patent system how few licences are in fact registered. One reason for this may not be generally appreciated. The Patent Office will not accept any document unless Inland Revenue stamp duty has been paid on it. The amount of duty payable depends on the type of document involved, and the rules are rather complex. To give an indication, an outright sale of industrial property rights carries a duty of 0.5 per cent if the consideration is between £5500 and £7000 and 1 per cent if it is more than £7000. For an agreement involving periodical payments of a specified amount (presumably including those providing for an annual minimum royalty) the duty is 2 per cent of the amount periodically payable. For agreements in which no quantifiable payment is specified but the transaction is certified to be worth less than £5500, there is a flat-rate duty of 50p if the agreement is under seal, but the old 6d stamp for agreements not under seal has been abolished. These figures are only intended to give a rough indication. The point to make is that the duty payable may amount to a noticeable sum of money, and is often difficult to determine. These factors tend to deter companies from having agreements stamped in return for the rather theoretical benefit of registering the assignment or licence at the Patent Office.

There is, of course, another reason for stamping, namely that if the document is the subject of a dispute in the courts, the latter may refuse to admit it in evidence if it is not properly stamped. The writer understands, however, that this technicality is unlikely to be used by counsel on either side. In any case it is always possible to stamp the document late provided a fee is paid of an amount up to the value of the stamp fee. This is unlikely to be significant if the document is the subject of a case in court.

TAXATION

Receipts under a licence are taxable like other income and the licensee can claim any royalty paid as a business expense. (An exception to the latter in the field of industrial property is the payment for the purchase of a trade mark). A lump sum payment is regarded as capital if it is for the purchase of know-how, or an assignment of or an exclusive licence under a patent, or an irrevocable non-exclusive licence; otherwise it is regarded as revenue. In the former case relief must be spread over the remaining life of the patent, or over six years in the case of know-how. If the payment counts as revenue, relief is due on the whole sum at once.

The licensee is obliged to withhold UK tax when paying royalties under patent licences (which implies the existence of a granted UK patent) but oddly enough not in respect of payments for know-how (including rights under patent applications not yet granted), trade-mark licences or licences under foreign patents.

Most other countries also provide for withholding tax. Where payments are made from one country to another subject to withholding tax, the recipient generally has to pay tax in his own country. He can, however, offset any withholding tax against his tax payments, under the double taxation agreement which normally exists between the two countries concerned, or in some countries (for example, the UK) by virtue of a unilateral concession where there is no double taxation agreement with the licensee's country (India for example).

Sometimes the licensor presses for payments "free of tax". Before the licensee agrees to this it is important for him to realise that where the payment is subject to withholding tax he will in effect be paying the grossed-up amount of the agreed sum — the latter to the licensor and the tax to the revenue authority.

If the financial provisions of an agreement are at all complex, a variety of tax problems may arise. The subject is, of course, highly specialised and complex, and all but the simplest agreements should be referred to a tax expert for advice. One set of difficulties of a kind familiar to businessmen can arise in connection with transactions with overseas subsidiaries. A transfer of rights in either direction should be at market value (estimated as best one can) in order to avoid tax problems.

OTHER TYPES OF AGREEMENT

The problems of drafting licence agreements are those of expressing in clear and unambiguous terms promises of a kind that can be enforced by the customary processes of the law. It is hoped that the brief references above to some of the typical problems will give the reader an insight into the way the draftsman approaches the task.

Problems of a different order often arise when we consider other types of agreement in which a collaborative element predominates rather than the promise-for-a-promise attitude of the traditional contract. Sometimes it almost seems that businessmen are frustrated in their attempt to define modes of collaboration by the interdiction of their own lawyers.

Secrecy agreements

On the face of it these are very simple documents. *A* agrees to pass to *B* his know-how in a particular field and *B* undertakes to keep this know-how secret so long as it is truly confidential, and not to use it except for some specified purpose. As indicated in earlier chapters, the sting is in the tail, because once *B* has learnt the information he cannot unlearn it. He cannot avoid making use of it as part of his mental equipment unless he forsakes that field of technology altogether. Another difficulty is that in many cases, the use to which *A* is willing to allow *B* to put the know-how is inherently incapable of definition at least in terms of a simple written agreement; it is often part of a wider collaboration which it is not expedient or practicable to write into the agreement. These problems on the use of know-how in secrecy agreements do not seem to have any drafting solutions.

Joint research agreements

As indicated above, the strictly enforceable contract element in technological collaboration agreements usually boils down to mutual undertakings to communicate research results and know-how in a defined field and to keep such information secret so long as it is truly confidential (see page 148). In such cases the difficulty just referred to of defining the use to which the know-how was to be put is often not significant because it is unnecessary to say anything about use, the value which *A* receives from being able to use *B*'s know-how tending to cancel out with the reciprocal value *B* obtains from *A*.

A connected problem is the ownership of and rights accruing to the parties under any industrial projects generated by the collaboration. As indicated in Chapter 4, if there is a clear geographical or technological line of division between the parties, the solution usually adopted is for each party to have exclusive rights in his own territory and/or technological field. If the split is territorial, this can be effected by giving ownership of the property to each party in his own territory — that is, *A* keeps the property generated by himself in his territory and assigns it to *B* in *B*'s territory and vice versa. This type of solution is not normally practicable if the line of division is technological. It is in fact preferable in either case for the matter to be dealt with by the grant of exclusive licences from *A* to *B* and vice versa, since these can easily be given any desired duration — for example, the term of the collaboration agreement.

If there is no clear line of division, the parties must normally each have joint rights of exploitation. This can be done either by *A* and *B* becoming joint patentees or by *A* granting *B* a sole licence under *A*'s patents and vice versa. The rights of joint patentees are referred to in Chapter 1.

In these situations it is usual to provide for possible disagreement between the parties about where and to what extent money should be spent on patenting. The best answer is usually a clause on the lines indicated above under "Patent Costs" (pages 150-1).

Apportionment of the benefit

The arrangements discussed above provide rather simplistic solutions which are adequate if the contributions by the parties to the collaboration are expected to be about equal, so that if the parties emerge with equal benefits in their own territories, at least rough justice is done.

In some cases, however, the nature of the collaboration, or the disparity of the contributions put in by the two parties, makes it necessary to provide for an unequal apportionment of the benefit. It is in such cases that the problem referred to at the beginning of this section — that of making an enforceable agreement at all — really begins to matter. Some of the types of situation where this can arise were discussed in Chapter 4. Perhaps the best case to illustrate the point is a collaboration to carry out trials in a field of use (see page 83).

Let us imagine that *A* is a chemical manufacturer without any interest or experience in the pharmaceutical field; *B* is a pharmaceutical company. *A* and *B* would like an agreement whereby *A* submits lists of chemical compounds to *B* and *B* evaluates them for pharmaceutical use. *A* is entitled to any patents for the compound itself and for its method of manufacture; *B* to any patents for pharmaceutical uses and for formulations. If *B* establishes that a compound *X* is of value and worth promoting commercially as a drug, both parties will expect to get some benefit.

The problem is that, at the time *A* and *B* are negotiating the agreement, it is beyond the wit of man to lay down an equitable division of the profits, because the nature of the successful compound, its pharmaceutical use, its methods of formulation and promotion and the size of the market in various countries are completely unknown. Likewise the contributions which *A* and *B* will have made to the outcome are unknown except that it is known that *B*'s contribution is almost certain to be greater than *A*'s by a factor of the order of at least 100 (say £500,000 to a few thousands).

Probably *A* would be satisfied if he could be sure of monopolising the supply of *X* to *B*, but anti-trust law and also commercial considerations prevent this unless *X* is patentable in itself — which is quite likely not to be the case (another unknown factor). On the other hand, *B* will not wish to risk being held to ransom in the supply of *X* if it is indeed patentable.

What can the parties do except to say that when and if a successful compound is found they will endeavour to come to an agreement on how to exploit it? An "agreement to agree" of such a blatant character would never get past the respective legal departments; they would indeed be justified in saying that it had no real meaning.

Another possibility which might be explored is to set out the criteria for the negotiation of an eventual agreement for exploitation in terms of the present intentions of the parties. Such intentions might be expressed as follows: the parties would cost according to specified criteria (these should not be too difficult to define) the research and development that they respectively put into the product; they would estimate, again according to agreed criteria, the profits they respectively make in each year of the exploitation of the product (*A* by sale of *X* and *B* by sale of the drug containing *X*); the aggregate profits would be redistributed in the same proportion as the research costs; and *B* would seek to arrive at an agreement with *A* for the purchase of its requirements of *X* from *A*. The parties would thus write into the original collaboration agreement an undertaking to use their best endeavours to conclude an exploitation agreement on the lines indicated above in the event of a successful compound being found.

It will be understood that there are far too many unknowns and uncertainties in these intentions to give any legal certainty to the undertaking, but it is suggested that the arrangement might be a kind of half-way house between a legally enforceable contract and a completely undefined situation. In effect the parties would have gone as far as they could to provide for the future eventuality, but what is the value of it if it cannot be enforced? It is thought that there are ethical and social forces, acting both on public companies and individuals employed in those companies, which tend to make them keep faith with an undertaking which has been properly negotiated and recorded as part of an overall agreement. When implementing this undertaking by negotiating the eventual exploitation agreement, they would at least start out with a predisposition to fulfil the intentions set out in the original collaboration agreement and would not wish to incur the odium of going back on their undertaking to do so.

The idea expressed above is not new. Businessmen are constantly signing "letters of intent", and making gentlemen's agreements, which depend on ethical and social rather than legal cautions. I am merely suggesting an extension of this type of practice to the uncertain situations which may arise in the implementation of otherwise fully enforceable collaboration agreements.

INDEMNITIES

It was explained in Chapter 4 that the licensee often requests an assurance that the licensee will not infringe any third party's patent. In some cases such an assurance may take the form of a request that the licensee indemnify (or "hold harmless") the licensor against any action for infringement of a third party's patent. The licensor may feel he knows enough about possible third party patents (or rather their absence) to risk giving such an indemnity, but he should realise that he could be letting himself in for a big liability. To fight an infringement action would be likely to cost a five figure sum while to settle it on terms such that the licensee would have to cease manufacture would involve compensation related to loss of profit, i.e. larger by a factor of say 2 or 3 than any royalty the licensor could have received.

There is another aspect of indemnification which, while not part of licensing as such, involves commercial agreements concerned with patents and is worth mentioning here. We refer to the indemnity against third party patents which customers often expect to get from suppliers. If the goods supplied are themselves the subject of a third party patent then it is natural and probably agreed tacitly, that it is the supplier rather than the customer who should be responsible vis-à-vis the patentee. The position is rather different, however, if the third party patent known or presumed to exist relates to the use of unpatented goods, e.g. a patented process for using unpatented plant or patented formulation using an unpatented ingredient *X*. Here the person responsible in law is the customer and the supplier will only be willing to take on the burden if the supply contract makes it worthwhile. The size of the burden is related to the amount of patent infringement represented by a given consignment of the goods. In the case of the supply of *X*, any given consignment represents only a small amount of risk in terms of infringement and the supplier can relieve himself of further risk by ceasing to supply the goods as soon as the patentee shows signs of starting trouble. At the other extreme — plant which will be used for many years — the risk per consignment, as it were, will be considerable. It is thus fairly easy for the supplier in the first type of case, but not in the second, to indemnify the customer.

Chapter 7

Sources of technology other than manufacturing companies

This book is primarily concerned with explaining to managers those aspects of licensing which are not part of the "second nature" of managers as businessmen. First and foremost this means the process of forming the legal relationships which constitute the licence agreement. Before this stage is reached, however, there must be two parties wishing to enter into such a relationship, and managers are exposed to a fairly copious literature advising them of the value of doing so, that is to say, of adopting an active policy of licensing their technology. Much of this seems to be propagandist rather than factual and Chapter 3 attempted to rationalise the matter and put it into perspective in terms of the function of a private-enterprise manufacturing company, which is to manufacture goods and sell them at a profit. The discussion there showed that, contrary to much that is said and written, it is licensing-in which may be a fundamental part of a company's development plan, while licensing-out can only (apart from one or two special exceptions, such as inventions for customer use) be secondary to the ultimate purpose of the company's research and development effort — that of making and selling goods.

Every licence in, however, involves a licence out, and there are some organisations that develop technology for the specific purpose of licensing it. Others act as middlemen or brokers in the licensing of technology. Managers seeking to buy technology may find themselves dealing with such organisations. Yet another type of licensing partner is the government or quasi-government body such as nationalised industries, government research stations and the semi-industrial, semi-government research associations. Managers should know something of the set-up, attitudes and policies of any of these organisations with which they may contemplate dealing. Allied to the setting up of legal relations with such bodies is the placing of contracts for sponsored or grant-aided research with universities and other research-oriented organisations, and the acquisition of rights from individual inventors, including "private inventors" and employees.

ORGANISATIONS AND THEIR MOTIVATIONS

The organisations with which the private-enterprise manufacturing company may become involved in licensing matters range from those staffed wholly or mainly by the civil service, such as the Science Research Council with its research stations including the National Physical Laboratory and many others, to private-enterprise research and consultant companies. The main types of organisation can be listed as follows:

1 Organisations staffed wholly or mainly by government employees: mainly research stations belonging to defence departments or the SRC, with the Royal Aeronautical Establishment and the NPL as probably the best known

2 The Medical and Agricultural Research Councils which are financed by the government but whose staff are not direct government employees in the sense of being civil servants

3 Statutory corporations: the National Research Development Corporation, the Atomic Energy Authority and the nationalised industries, and their counterparts abroad
4 The Research Associations, each of which is financed jointly by the SRC and its industrial membership
5 The universities and other academic institutions which, although autonomous, receive a large component of public money.
6 Organisations financed wholly by private money which act as consultants and carry out sponsored research and sometimes research on their own account

The financial interest of all these organisations is in favour of their licensing their technology since they are not, in so doing, creating competition for themselves. However, the degree of enthusiasm with which such matters are pursued varies a good deal from one type of organisation to another, depending mainly on the attitudes of the individuals who actually generate the technology.

Academic inventors generally like to see their inventions put to use, but on the whole prefer not to be directly involved in the commercial mechanics whereby this is accomplished. Civil service and other inventors paid by the government tend to take a similar view, the reluctance to become involved in exploitation being most marked in the case of the Medical Research Council. This attitude has, however, never been universal. Before the war it was the general policy of the government to allow civil service inventors to retain the commercial rights in their inventions, and a few (for example in the Post Office) took advantage of this to make some money by selling or licensing commercial rights to industrial companies. By and large, however, academic inventors would merely publish their research and leave whoever might be interested to cash in on any commercial applications. As is well known, this attitude began to disintegrate when the discovery of penicillin was commercially exploited on a major scale without any financial benefit flowing to the discoverer, his organisation or initially to industrial companies in the UK.

One of the reasons for setting up the NRDC was to provide academic inventors with a non-commercial agency for exploiting their inventions. Another object was to provide a repository for the commercial rights in government inventions, thus enabling the government to do away with the somewhat anomolous right of the inventors to engage in commercial exploitation on their own account.

A third function of the NRDC is to provide finance for the development of inventions which individual commercial companies are not prepared to take up, but which the NRDC considers could be a commercial success if some initial assistance were provided. Such inventions may come from the public sources mentioned above or from private sources, including individual "private inventors".

It is thought that this development function of the NRDC should be regarded as the provision of high-risk low-security finance for pump-priming purposes, on the basis of the skilled assessments and judgements of the NRDC staff. The finance is given to a company or other organisation (either already existing or set up for the purpose) entering into an agreement with the NRDC which provides for the development work to be carried out and for some proportion of any eventual income to be payable to the NRDC. The agreement could make provision for the ownership and exploitation of any industrial property which might arise from the development and would thus incorporate the appropriate features of licence and allied agreements set forth in earlier chapters.

The government has in recent years started a scheme for making grants to industry for carrying out civilian (as opposed to defence) research and development. The standard contract for such a grant would provide for a payment to be made to the government from any profits that might be made by the grantee, either from his own exploitation or by granting licences. The right of free Crown use would also be reserved, as in any case where government money is provided.

The nationalised industries may appear as licensors first in respect of technology having applications outside their own field and second in an attempt to exploit technology in their own field outside the UK. In a somewhat intermediate position between the nationalised industries and the development side of the NRDC is the Atomic Energy Authority, which recently began to promote a policy of applying its technological resources to collaboration with industrial partners on the basis of agreements providing for a share of any eventual income to be paid to the AEA. Naturally the nationalised industries can appear also as buyers or licensees of technology from private industrial companies.

The statutory corporations we are discussing — NRDC, nationalised industries and UKAEA (the latter in its guise of collaborator with industry) — are charged with the duty of serving the public interest but also of balancing income and outgoings at least in the long term. Since the corporations (with one or two exceptions) operate in areas of low or no profitability, the second duty in practice means a struggle to secure the maximum income. This, however, conflicts with the duty of serving the public interest. It follows that the managers and executives of the corporations are constantly having to use their judgement collectively and individually to strike a balance between their two conflicting duties.

To put it another way, the financial discipline acting on the organisation and the individuals in it is tempered by the need to serve the public interest as the corporation sees it. Somewhat paradoxically, however, the corporations tend to be tougher in licence negotiations, other things being equal, than most private companies. This is partly, no doubt, an example of the fact that the more detached one is about the outcome, the stronger is one's negotiating position. In addition there is the psychological effect of the actual or imagined backing of the government itself behind the corporations. A third reason for what is generally regarded as a particularly tough attitude by the NRDC, is the fact that it is in the business of acquiring and licensing inventions in a bigger way (at least quantitatively) than any other organisation.

Yet another factor which may cause difficulties in negotiations with a public corporation is the conflict between the need which is usually felt, and often exists in reality, for the licensee to have exclusivity, and the attempt by the corporation to avoid favouring one private company at the expense of another. So far as the NRDC is concerned, this by no means prevents the granting of exclusivity, but it makes it harder for the prospective licensee to obtain such a concession.

To set against these factors favourable to the negotiating position of the corporation we must not forget the ultimate sanction of parliamentary control. In practice this can operate in favour of the private individual or company negotiator in that he or it can refer any obviously oppressive attitude to an interested member of parliament who can exert influence on the relevant government department, culminating in the weapon of a parliamentary question. The effect of a "PQ" on a public corporation should not be underestimated.

MIDDLEMEN IN LICENSING

If we regard the NRDC's activities as divided between the exploitation of inventions in the form they are received on the one hand and the development of inventions on the other, the former can be considered as analogous to that of the private enterprise "patent broker". In both cases the organisation is acting as a middleman between the inventor and the prospective commercial user of the invention. There is in general, however, a difference in the modus operandi of the two. NRDC acquires the property in the invention on revenue-sharing terms as a precondition of exploiting it, whereas the broker, as the name implies, acts strictly as an intermediary, the negotiations taking place between the inventor and the prospective licensee.

SOURCES OF INVENTIONS FOR LICENSING

How do the NRDC and patent brokers rate as sources of technology for shoppers and prospective buyers? There is in fact no shortage of inventions on offer in various ways. Some technical journals publish lists of inventions available for licensing and there is of course the list of patents which have been endorsed, "licences of right" (see Chapter 6), appearing week by week in the *Official Journal* of the Patent Office. Between ten and twenty of these appear in each issue of the *Journal*. Patentees may also insert advertisements in the *Official Journal* or the technical press, or circulate an offer to possibly interested companies, these activities usually being undertaken to forestall a charge of "abuse of monopoly" (see Chapter 5). It is often the view of those concerned with licensing that any invention which is dealt with in one of these ways is most unlikely to be worth considering by a prospective licensee.

At the other end of the scale is the item of technology which is singled out and made the subject of an active selling effort. Such an item is prima facie worth serious consideration.

The NRDC or the private broker may vary their selling approach in respect of the various inventions in their portfolios between a routine listing on the one hand and an active promotion on the other. In the case of the NRDC, the vehicle for the routine listing, and in some cases also for one facet of an active promotion, is the Bulletin circulated free of charge at regular intervals to the majority of companies in the UK. The patent broker proceeds in a similar way, except that he may charge a fee for his bulletin. Alternatively he may make retainer agreements with a number of companies whereby he undertakes to circulate to each a selection of inventions which he thinks may interest that particular company. The amount of the fee would depend on whether the company had exclusivity in respect of the lists circulated to it (at least for an initial period, for example, on a first-refusal basis).

There is usually one of two reasons for using a middleman for licensing. The first is that the originator of the technology is unable or unwilling to engage in commercial exploitation. This applies to most of the NRDC's sources. The second is that particular inventions may not arouse the enthusiasm required to motivate the originating company to make the effort necessary for direct exploitation. It is also, of course, possible for a company to feel a need for the expertise of the specialist in the exploitation of inventions.

ACQUISITION OF INVENTIONS

An invention prima facie belongs to the inventor and will not vest in a company or corporation without an operation of the law, whether explicit or implicit, which is called an "assignment". As mentioned above, a broker acting solely as an intermediary will not take an assignment but will simply make an agreement with the inventor (or other proprietor if the inventor has already assigned his rights) whereby the broker undertakes to seek a licensee, usually on an exclusive agency basis, in return for a consideration which will normally be based on a percentage of any royalty or like income from the eventual licence. The broker may also charge an initial lump-sum fee for taking the invention on his books.

The NRDC has a standard revenue-sharing agreement under which it takes assignment of inventions offered to it. The basis of this is the payment to the inventor of 50 per cent of any net revenue earned by the invention after deduction of patent and possibly certain other expenses, with an advance payment of 5 per cent of gross revenue which is set off against the eventual payment from the net (if any). The question also arises in the case of inventions from organisations such as universities (where the inventor is not primarily paid to make inventions or may indeed be a student) what rights if any accrue to the university. This is referred to on pages 176-7.

In the case of inventors paid wholly out of government money, the NRDC obtains assignment free of charge, but if there is any commercial exploitation, the inventor can apply for an award which would normally be a substantial percentage of any revenue earned, and would be paid by the NRDC out of such revenue. It should also be noted that a standard condition of the assignment would be the reservation of free user rights by the Crown, and these would carry through to any licence eventually granted by the NRDC.

There is no obligation on inventors or their organisations to offer their inventions to the NRDC, and some universities in particular have set up their own parallel organisations, often directed, however, primarily to dealing with cases in which a grant from an industrial company is involved.

Research aided by industry

The importance to the industrial company of the terms on which the NRDC acquires inventions lies primarily in the fact that in its dealings with academic inventors such a company tends to be in competition, overt or implicit, with NRDC. As this body is such a large dealer in inventions, its terms tend to be regarded as the norm. This has a significant effect on the attitude of academic workers who are in receipt of grants from industry, and it is often necessary for the manager responsible for making the grant to explain to the grantee that the standard NRDC terms are offered to inventors who have received *no* grant from NRDC.

The relationship between the grantor and grantee really involves a contract between them, one element of which (whether express or implied) is the ownership of any industrial property that may arise from the grant-aided or sponsored work. Since many of the principles of licensing and allied agreements discussed in earlier chapters apply to such a contract, it is appropriate to discuss the matter in this work. Before doing so it will be convenient to deal with the rights in inventions made by employees, since this is, of course, the commonest situation, and failure to understand it properly often leads to confusion in considering grant-aided inventions.

EMPLOYEE'S INVENTIONS

The basic point which is often misunderstood or overlooked is that the ownership of an invention made by an employee is a matter of contract. This confusion is generally due to the fact that under common law any service agreement (contract) which is silent on the point is deemed to include an implied term that inventions made by the employee "in the course of his employment" belong to the employer. This phrase conceals two requirements; first, that the employee's job is of a kind in which innovations in his employer's business are liable to arise — for example, a research worker or a development engineer; second, that the particular invention in question did in fact arise out of the job. Provided these requirements are met the employer is automatically entitled to the benefit of the invention or, in the legal jargon, he is the "beneficial owner". This does not, however, give him the right to apply for a patent, since that belongs to the inventor (or inventors jointly if there is more than one).

Nevertheless the employing company may apply for the patent provided the right to apply has been assigned to it by the inventor(s). This assignable right was first created by the 1949 Patents Act and there was some dispute at the time about the form the assignment should take, but it is thought to be generally accepted now that a simple declaration by the inventor of his assent to the making of the application, for example as set out at the end of the official Patent Application Form, operates as a valid assignment of the right to apply. It should be noted, however, that this affects only the legal title and has no effect on the beneficial ownership of the invention. If the case is one to which the common law doctrine referred to above applies, an assignment of the beneficial ownership is not strictly necessary, although it is prudent to secure one as an acknowledgement by the employee that the invention does fall in this category.

It is, of course, possible to make terms with an employee different from that implied under common law. For example, a prospective employee in a particularly strong bargaining position may be able to negotiate for a royalty payment under any invention he makes in the course of his employment. The Patents Act (*s*56) provides machinery for resolving disputes between employer and employee including the making of an apportionment between them, but the House of Lords has held that only a legally enforceable agreement will enable the Court to make such an apportionment, otherwise the invention belongs wholly to the employer if made in the course of employment or wholly to the employee if not.

In some countries, notably Germany and the Scandinavian countries, the employee inventor is automatically entitled to a reward for his invention. There is some political urge in the UK in favour of such a provision but those with experience of these matters tend to feel that the making of a patentable invention as made in industry is nearly always part of a team effort to which a range of other employees contribute directly or indirectly, and that to single out the "inventor" for special treatment would only lead to bad feeling.

SPONSORED RESEARCH

Once it has been grasped that employee inventions belong to the employer only because the law looks at *service* contracts in a special and exceptional way, it will be understood that where the relationship between the person providing the money (let us say a sponsor or grantor) and the inventor is not that of employer and employee, there is no automatic right to the invention by the sponsor or grantor. In such cases the courts would adhere to the usual practice of not implying terms into a contract which are not implied by the contract itself.

Thus, any agreement between a sponsor and a consultant or similar organisation for carrying out research, even if the latter is paid for wholly by the sponsor, should make explicit provision for the ownership of any resulting industrial property. Normally, in the circumstances envisaged, the whole of the rights should belong to the sponsor without further payment, and the agreement should so state. It is, however, important to define exactly which inventions qualify for this treatment. The easiest and commonest way of doing this is to define the inventions as any which "arise out of the sponsored research". While this is no doubt adequate in many cases, it is not a perfect answer. The reason for this is that in nearly every case the consultant will be engaged in other projects besides the one in question, and it is impossible for him to divide his mind into watertight compartments. He may hit on an inventive idea which he cannot easily allocate to a particular project. It is therefore advisable to try to make a definition of the relevant technological field (an exercise referred to frequently in this book) and to provide that any invention or other industrial property generated by the consultant in this field during the term of the agreement shall belong to the sponsor. The consultant's willingness to agree to such a provision will depend on the accuracy with which the definition of the field can be framed.

While the agreement should be accurate, it need not be formal. It is usually best for psychological reasons to put agreements of the type referred to in this and the next section in the form of letters to be countersigned by the consultant or grantee.

GRANT-AIDED RESEARCH

There are two main types of recipients of research grants from industry: government organisations and universities. The essence of this situation from the present point of view is that the grant represents only a part of the resources which go into the project, the grantee making a substantial contribution in the form of overheads and access to a pool of knowledge and experience. It is therefore not a foregone conclusion that the grantee will automatically concede the rights to the grantor free of charge.

In the case of government organisations, standard forms of contract have been laid down and there is usually no effective room for negotiation. Briefly, the sort of terms the grantor may expect to be "offered" will be one of two alternatives, depending on the relative weight of the contributions from the grantor and the government establishment. Either the grantor will acquire the rights subject to free use by the Crown and an obligation to license on reasonable terms any firm nominated by the government department concerned; or the government will retain the rights subject to the grantor's right to a free non-exclusive licence in the UK, and to licences abroad on terms to be decided by the government department.

In the case of university and other academic institutions, however, the negotiating initiative usually lies with the grantor. The main danger here is the temptation to suppose that the disposal of industrial property rights can safely be left to look after itself, at least until the project is under way. It is quite possible that in particular cases no provision need, or should, be made, but this ought to be arrived at by a consideration of the factors involved, not merely by default. In favour of making no provision would be a motivation for making the grant which is primarily concerned with fostering goodwill — for example, for future recruitment or to secure an entrée to the department. In such a case haggling for industrial property rights could destroy the very objective of the grant.

Against this must be weighed the likelihood that an important invention might arise, the value of which might outweigh the goodwill consideration. The decision whether or not to put terms about industrial property rights into the contract must depend on a consideration of factors such as these, but if the decision is to make no provision, the grantor's position is not irretrievably lost. It simply means that if a valuable invention does arise he must negotiate for the rights from scratch. Experience shows, however, that the fact that an inventor is an academic worker and is in receipt of a grant does not necessarily mean that he will adopt a reasonable attitude in such negotiations. Cases have indeed occurred where the grantor has been held to ransom, even to the extent of making him bid against a competitor.

If the decision is to make provision for industrial property rights, a proposal should be put to the grantee at the time the grant is negotiated. Three types of situation can be distinguished:

1 The direction and outcome of the research can be estimated to an extent that enables a reasonable forecast to be made of the nature of any invention that may arise and its commercial value. In such a case the inventor can be offered a down-payment for the rights or a royalty on use of the invention. It is impossible to generalise about which form of payment is likely to be most advantageous for one or the other party. If the grant is made to a research student or junior assistant, it may be possible to settle for a down-payment of £100—£200, and this is likely to be more favourable to the grantor than any royalty payment. If, however, a substantially greater sum would be required to reach agreement, a royalty is likely (but not necessarily) to be looked on more favourably by the grantor.

The point of time at which any downpayment should be made must be considered. A suitable arrangement is for payment when the grantor at its discretion files a UK patent application. If, however, the agreed sum is to be large, a proportion could be held back until later in the development of the idea — for example, when the grantor decides to enter it in its own laboratories as a development project.

2 The nature of the outcome is uncertain, but the known commercial position in relation to the field of research makes it possible to say that a small royalty (say 1 per cent on turnover) would not damage the use of any resulting invention. In such a case it may be reasonable to settle terms in spite of the uncertainty. To make this comparative with the NRDC figure of 50 per cent of the revenue from licensing it should be noted that if the grantor licenses the patent for 5 per cent of the turnover, the NRDC figure on a turnover basis is equivalent to 2½ per cent and the 1 per cent quoted above is equivalent to a share of revenue of 20 per cent.

3 The likely outcome is too uncertain for the parties to arrive at any agreement in advance. The only course then open is for the grantee to give the grantor "first refusal" of any rights which may arise. Reduced to legal terms this means that the grantee agrees at the outset that (i) he will not negotiate with anyone else until a given period has elapsed after, say, the filing of the patent application, and (ii) that if the company makes an offer he will not accept an offer from anyone else on less favourable terms. It should be borne in mind that it is no answer to the problem for the grantees it is not suggested that they will never be prepared since this is meaningless unless the terms of the proposed acquisition are specified.

In discussing terms which may be negotiated with academic grantees it is not suggested that they will never be prepared to let the grantor have the rights free of charge. Just as the grantor may in certain cases be willing to make no provision in advance, so the grantee may be prepared to agree in advance to assign all inventions without consideration other than the payment of the grant.

The person negotiating for the grant is usually the person who will carry out the research and/or his head of department. It is therefore important to take steps to ascertain what rights, if any, the university may claim. For this purpose the university may be invited either to be a party to the agreement or to signify its consent in writing. The latter course is usually sufficient, as the university is normally willing to waive any rights it might have in the grantee's work if an industrial company is providing funds. It should be noted that if the inventor is a student rather than a member of the staff, the university may not have any rights to waive, but this matter also should be cleared in advance. The question of the NRDC may crop up and it should be borne in mind that the NRDC has no prior right to inventions arising from research to which it has not subscribed. Sometimes their standard terms of sharing revenue equally with the inventor are quoted, but they provide no guide to the terms which a grantor should offer, since as mentioned above they apply in the case where the NRDC has *not* contributed to the research.

Sometimes the research is supported by a grant from government sources (this term does not include the NRDC) in addition to the grant from the grantor company. It is thought that there are no standard forms for this situation, but that normally the government will claim no benefit from any resulting industrial property rights. A special case is that of the "Cooperative Awards in Pure Science" (CAPS) scheme run by the Department of Trade and Industry. Here the monetary contribution of the industrial "cooperating body" is only nominal, its main contribution being to give the grantee access to its laboratories, works and confidential information and experience. It is understood that the Department is prepared to allow the grantee and the cooperating body to negotiate terms for the transfer of any industrial property rights, and will normally approve the resulting agreement without claiming any rights for itself.

A necessary part of any agreement with academic scientists is provision for eventual publication of the results of the research. A satisfactory arrangement is to provide that the grantee makes regular reports to the grantor and does not publish any item until, say, six months after it has been reported. This gives time for the grantor to file a patent application if it wishes and does not materially delay publication, since it would normally take at least that time for matter submitted to a technical journal to be published.

PRIVATE INVENTORS

Most companies from time to time receive submissions of inventions "out of the blue" from private inventors who are not in any contractual relationship with the company. The general experience is that the man working outside any industrial or research organisation is too far removed from the real-life problems of industry to produce any ideas of practical value. At all events he has to surmount a high barrier of scepticism before he can arouse any interest. Even if he succeeds in doing so, the market value of an idea which has been developed no further than a private inventor's laboratory (or even armchair) is very low. After doing the rounds of industry, a private inventor may approach the NRDC, but here again only a very small proportion of such inventions are taken up. On the other hand the NRDC appears to provide some assurance that inventions which are important, but too revolutionary to appeal to the existing industry, will not fall by the wayside, the classical case being the hovercraft.

The principles described in earlier sections apply to the negotiation of an agreement with a private inventor. The company will want to insist on securing an outright assignment of all the rights from the inventor. Occasionally it will retain his services as a consultant, but more often the main preoccupation will be to prevent the inventor from being in a position to interfere in the development of the invention.

Paradoxically the main difficulty in negotiating with a private inventor is the weakness of his position relative to that of the company. It can be taken for granted that if the company does succeed in commercialising the invention, the inventor will grossly over-estimate the value of his initial contribution in comparison with the research, development and promotional work put in by the company. Thus, however generous the terms originally negotiated with the inventor, he is almost certain to be profoundly dissatisfied once commercial success has been achieved, and he will find no difficulty at all in mobilising the support of the popular press and broadcasting commentators in publicising his disillusionment. The likelihood of something of this sort taking place increases the barrier which a private inventor has to overcome in interesting a company in his idea.

Another obstacle to easy relations between a large company and the private inventor is the fact that if the company receives a submission and after investigation rejects it, there is a presumption in the mind of the outsider that any subsequent use of something similar stemmed from the submission and that the company has therefore acted fraudulently. Even if, as people in industry know is at least equally likely, an employee of the company who knew nothing of the submission thought of the idea independently, this may be hard to prove, and the whole situation is likely to lead to embarrassment if not litigation, with public opinion always ready to support the "little man". In an attempt to forestall this kind of difficulty, companies will refuse to look at a submission unless the inventor has filed a patent application, thus defining his rights at the time when the submission is made. Some big companies which receive a large number of submissions go further and set up a procedure whereby any submission is returned unread, together with a form for signature by the inventor whereby he waives any claim against the company for subsequent use of the idea, unless such use infringes any patent eventually obtained by the inventor. If the inventor accepts this condition he returns the submission with the signed waiver. The writer is not aware of any case in which the courts have considered such a situation, but if it upheld the waiver, the company could, in spite of it (or perhaps even because of it), find itself subject to adverse publicity in favour of the "little man" who was tricked into waiving his rights by one of the Goliaths of industry.

Chapter 8

Negotiations

This chapter is concerned with the way in which a licence contract is *formed*. To some extent it will go again over ground explored in Chapter 2 to help explain the *nature* of the contractual relationship. Chapter 2 established, for example, that in spite of appearances to the contrary, a contract is not meaningful unless it is made against a background of conflicting interests. Reduced to its bare essentials, it means in colloquial terms that *A* has or will have something *B* wants and *B* has or will have something *A* wants and they agree to swap. In terms of licensing, again reduced to the bare essentials of a simple patent licence, *A* has a piece of technological territory in which *B* wants to work in order to generate income, and *A* wants a share of that income.

THE STARTING POSITIONS

To commence negotiating a contract, each party must have something which he can unequivocally give or withhold at his will. It is true that if a patentee withholds a licence he may be vulnerable to an application for a compulsory licence, but it is his privilege to do so if he wants. Likewise the prospective licensee is entirely free to decline the licence. This, however, is only one side of the coin. The other is what each party would lose by withholding what the other one wants. There is obviously a great deal of difference in the negotiating position of a patentee that is a large corporation for which the income from the proposed licence is only of marginal significance, and the one who is an individual inventor with no other source of income.

Each negotiator must therefore take into account not only what he would gain by securing the consideration offered by the other, but also what the other would lose by failing to secure his part of the bargain. It is at this point that any inequality between the parties becomes significant. Chapter 2 referred to Esau as being an inept negotiator, but this was hardly fair. The disadvantage to Esau of not concluding the contract with Jacob would have been that he would have gone hungry, and this is a much more potent factor in affecting the way negotiations are conducted than the possibility of acquiring some future property right, which was all Jacob had to lose.

In the case of patent licences such a stark disparity is unlikely to arise (though in harsher times it was by no means impossible for an inventor to die in a garret for failure to negotiate a return for his invention), but gross inequalities can still occur, for instance between a "private inventor" and a large company or other organisation. As pointed out in Chapter 7, the private inventor is almost bound to feel that the bargain he made with an organisation which successfully exploits his invention was unfair, because he regards his contribution as so much the more important. There is, however, usually another reason for the inventor's dissatisfaction — the basic inequality between the parties, which was reflected in their respective negotiating positions. The bargain was made between an individual without the means to get his invention beyond the first experimental stage and an organisation to which the whole matter was of quite small significance — one of a large number of other possible developments. If negotiation means anything, it must reflect this inequality, and the law will uphold the resulting contract without regard to the reasons why the parties originally found it acceptable or to the change in circumstances which has since made one of them wish to repudiate it.

NEGOTIATING POWER

The object of a negotiation is to persuade the other party to part with his property or other legal right for as little as possible. It is essentially the action of one individual (or team) on the mind of the other, and vice versa. Psychological factors are therefore paramount. For example, it is much easier to negotiate a royalty of 1 per cent on the price of petrol than 500 per cent on the value of an additive to the petrol, even if the two alternatives are calculated to result in the payment of exactly the same sum of money. Thus, in licensing, the weapons available to a negotiator are the power of his personality, his detachment (or his ability to feign detachment) from the outcome, and the deployment of convincing arguments. The last two may conflict, for example, if it is necessary for the negotiator to demonstrate his enthusiasm for working under a licence.

ARGUMENTATION

There would be no point in arguments put forward by *A* if they were not directed to proving to *B* that *A*'s terms are to the advantage of *B*. If they were directed to proving *A*'s advantage, they would be rejected by *B* out of hand. Since, however, if *A* is trying to persuade *B* to agree to a term *B* does not want to agree to, it can only be because that term is to *A*'s advantage, we have the paradoxical situation that *A* is using arguments to support a term favourable to himself by proving that it is favourable to *B*. This is one of the reasons why a good negotiator will generally try to minimise the conflict and maximise the common interest between the parties. Moreover between businessmen, especially managers in large companies, there are certain conventions of behaviour amounting almost to rules by which the game is played. The highest score goes to the negotiator who appears to be considerate of the other side's interest and diffident of his own, and also to the one who is able to put up the more successful debating performance; the lowest to the one who appears to take an aggressive line, or who cannot give rational answers to the other side's arguments purporting to be in his favour, even though he knows perfectly well that he is the best judge of his own interests. It may be said that these factors are psychological rather than "real", but negotiations are in truth only a mental process, the object being to make the other party say "yes" by mental persuasion, so that it is indeed the psychological factors which count.

CONFLICT AND COLLABORATION

The appearance of a community of interest which is developed by the parties as a by-product of the negotiating process can become intertwined with a genuine community of interest that can arise for material or objective reasons. Chapter 2 showed the underlying truth behind the businessman's cliche that an agreement remains valid in practice only as long as the parties both want to implement it. This is especially so where an important term of the agreement is to carry out some kind of collaboration, but may be true to some extent even where there is no such term. There are also cases in which one party's advantage is not wholly the other's disadvantage. The best example of this is the level of royalty, where it is not to the licensor's advantage to insist on a royalty which would unduly hamper the licensee in exploiting the invention.

This conflict versus collaboration situation can be summed up by saying that most businessmen prefer to work in a cooperative atmosphere rather than one of conflict, that the rules of the negotiating game tend to reflect this predilection, that to break the rules is to suffer embarrassment and a loss of "marks", and that there are sometimes material or objective as well as psychological factors which, to an extent depending on the type of agreement, favour cooperation. All these factors together tend to highlight the community of interest between the negotiating parties, but the successful negotiator will not allow himself to be carried away by this. He will bear in mind that at least in respect of some of the terms of the agreement, the interests of the parties conflict, and that if this were not so there would be no need for a negotiation.

PROCRASTINATION

One result of the euphoria surrounding negotiations, especially if they are carried on in congenial social surroundings, is the tendency to put off contentious issues until "more is known" about the operation of the licence. As was explained more fully in Chapter 2, if businessmen/negotiators are left to themselves they may very well fail to make a bargain at all; if they have made a bargain they are likely not to have defined it adequately, or it will include promises incapable of fulfilment for legal reasons; and they will most probably have failed to consider at all certain terms which, although somewhat abstruse, are nevertheless necessary to the agreement. It is for these reasons that professional help is needed, but the type of help required is not the same for the various defects noted above.

For the first, the primary requirement is somehow to discipline the negotiators to eschew procrastination and stay with it until a real bargain has been struck. For failure of definition, what is needed is an intimate discussion between the professional adviser and his client so that the former can get enough information to frame a definitive form of words on a realistic basis. The unfulfillable promise also needs close discussion of the commercial situation with the professional man to enable the businessman to recast his offer in a way which he really can implement. For the abstruse matters whose commercial importance does not match their legal complexity (as indicated elsewhere in this book), a professional man within the company should be appointed to deal with such matters on an executive basis. This is the "coordinator" referred to below.

PEOPLE INVOLVED AND HOW THEY OPERATE

The starting point of the negotiations to be described is that company *A* is interested in granting a licence and company *B* is interested in accepting this licence, provided mutually acceptable terms can be negotiated. What people in each company are involved in converting this interest into a completed agreement, and how do they perform their respective tasks? The people involved in each company are as follows:

1 The principal in charge of the negotiations. He will normally be a manager on the technical, development or marketing side of the business, although if a company has a lot of licensing business, a licensing manager specialising in negotiations may be appointed.

2 The lawyer, who is responsible for the preparation of the agreement document.

3 The industrial property specialist, normally a patent agent. His primary job is to advise on the nature and extent of the patents, trade marks and know-how involved in the deal, and to supply the technological backing and the knowledge of foreign industrial property law required to supplement the lawyer's expertise.

4 The tax expert who should advise on the tax aspects of the financial provisions of the agreement.

NEGOTIATIONS — THE WRONG WAY

It will be appreciated that with a manager and three experts, each belonging to strong but disparate disciplines, and all duplicated in the other company, firm steering is necessary to see the complex paperwork through to a successful conclusion in a reasonably efficient manner. Unfortunately this is often not achieved: the manager, although lacking the time and the inclination to attend to a job which does not really suit his capabilities, fails to realise that a coordinator who can take this task off his shoulders ought to be nominated. The result is a minuet that may, in a case of typical complexity, proceed on the following lines:

Stage 1 Manager *A* and Manager *B* discuss the broad commercial terms of the proposed agreement. It usually happens that at this stage the managers wish to avoid diluting the communication between them by introducing

Lawyer *A* and Lawyer *B*. As has been said frequently in this book, the approach of the lawyer is not only different from that of the manager but in some respects is contrary. It is often not an exaggeration to say that Manager *A* feels he has more in common with his "adversary" Manager *B* than with his own lawyer. Managers *A* and *B* accordingly prefer (as they hope) to reach agreement untrammelled by the legal niceties and then hand the matter over to their respective lawyers to prepare an agreement. The outcome is a letter written by Manager *A* (the licensor) to Manager *B* setting out in broad terms what they have agreed. This type of document is often referred to as the "heads of agreement". It is worth noting here that any such letter should contain some such phrase as "subject to agreement on the terms of a formal contract". This is to avoid the possibility of the heads of agreement being construed as a complete offer, which could be prematurely accepted by the other side so as to constitute a contract.

The time between the initial establishment of an interest and the sending of the letter setting out the broad terms of a licence agreement can be estimated at one to three months.

Stage 2 Manager *A* gives the heads of agreement to Lawyer *A* and asks for a draft agreement. Lawyer *A* considers the document and decides he needs further instructions on one or more points at which (in some of the ways indicated in Chapter 2) the wording is inadequate to enable him to prepare a draft.

Estimated time between receipt of heads of agreement and reference back to Manager *A*, one to two months.

Stage 3 *A* proposes a meeting with Manager *B* to clarify the heads of agreement, and this time they decide the lawyers should be present. Manager *B* (who has been waiting for *A*'s draft agreement) now puts the heads of agreement to Lawyer *B*. The date for the meeting is fixed, allowing for the four people and any supporting staff to be available, and for Lawyer *B* to have considered the heads.

Estimated time: one month.

Stage 4 The meeting takes place. Manager *A* takes the chair, but he is not sufficiently at home with the legal aspects to steer the meeting to the desired conclusion, which is the revision of the heads of agreement to a form in which they can be converted by Lawyer *A* into a draft agreement. The managers want to concentrate on the main issues but the lawyers tend to divert the discussion into matters of detail which they are naturally anxious to get settled, but which ought not to be taking up valuable meeting time. A good example which has been given elsewhere in this book is a discussion on what is to happen in the event of infringement by a third party of the patent to be licensed. If, on the other hand, the lawyers were not present, the managers might still fail to arrive at a point at which satisfactory drafting instructions can be given to the lawyer. In spite of some wasted time and frustration, the meeting does eventually reach this point.

Stage 5 Lawyer *A* produces Draft 1.
Estimated time: two months.

Stage 6 Draft 1 is considered within Company *A* before submission to Company *B*. For this purpose Lawyer *A* sends the draft to Manager *A* with copies to Patent Agent *A* and Taxman *A*. A "postal conference" ensues with a prolific supply of internal memoranda passing among the four people, those who have been asked to comment feeling they must at least say something. Even if there are no major points, a draft agreement always provides at least a few points of detail which can be criticised. Since there is no machinery for allocating the major points for decision by the manager and leaving the minor points for the professional advisers, the whole procedure is likely to be inefficient and frustrating, but in due course Lawyer *A* is in a position to prepare a revised version, Draft 2.
Estimated time: two months.

Stage 7 Draft 2 is sent to Company *B* and the process of consideration within *B* takes its course in a similar way to the consideration of Draft 1 in *A*. Eventually Lawyer *B*

prepares a re-draft or amendments which result in Draft 3.
Estimated time: three months.

Stage 8 Draft 3 is sent to *A* and the process of consideration is repeated. Another meeting between *A* and *B* may be arranged, or an amended document, Draft 4, sent to *B*.
Estimated time: three months.

Stage 9 Draft 4 is accepted by *B* after the usual consideration. Time: two to three months.

Stage 10 Draft 4 is engrossed by Lawyer *A* and executed by both parties.
Time : three months.

COORDINATION

Anyone who has been involved in this kind of exercise knows that it is highly inefficient. The time which it takes, estimated here at eighteen to twenty-two months, is alone evidence of this. There are two main reasons for the inefficiency: first, the managers are communicating with their lawyers across a gulf. The subject of the agreement is an item of new technology but a lawyer's education is unlikely to have included science. On the other hand the wording of the agreement is legal and the manager has had no education in the law. The result is that each is incapable of grasping the different frame of reference in which the other is working.

The second reason for inefficiency is the lack of adequate coordination of the complex work of consultation required for the preparation and amendment of the successive drafts, involving the work of four people in each company. What is needed is to allocate to one person the job of coordinating the whole procedure from the start, or at least from stage 2 onwards. The coordinator ideally needs the following qualifications:

1 He should be at ease in both the technological and legal frames of reference. This enables him to bridge the gap

between the manager and the lawyer and interpret each to the other.

2 He should be experienced in the art of taking an executive role in the sense of deciding which matters require reference to the manager in charge of the negotiation and which can be decided at the professional level. It should be noted that not only is it an inefficient use of the manager's time to refer all the minutiae of the agreement to him for decision; it is also counter-productive. The manager is unlikely to be prepared to spend the time necessary to grasp the significance of what are essentially legal points and his judgement on them is not likely to be as good as that of his professional advisers. The results of this are familiar: if, after the agreement has been concluded, reference has to be made to the wording of the agreement in order to resolve some difference or point of doubt, the manager concerned is often amazed at the significance of a form of words with which he had concurred when the agreement was in the course of preparation. A coordinator having the qualifications and experience specified here would in fact have been in a *better* position to interpret the company's interest on a point of the kind we are considering than the manager.

3 The third requirement for the coordinator is to have some knowledge of industrial property law in overseas countries as well as the UK, and also good channels of communication with industrial property experts in overseas countries with which the company's licence agreements will be concerned. He will then be able to make an initial appraisal of the impact of the local law on the type of business relationship which the company wishes to set up, and to supplement this by local advice as necessary.

4 The coordinator should be calendar-conscious, so that he will make an effort to ensure that the preparation of the agreement progresses on the commercial rather than the legal time scale.

Licensing executives

Efforts are currently being made to establish, as a professional entity, a body of specialists in the techniques of licensing, usually known when in the employment of an industrial company as "licensing executives". The term "licensing executive" has not been used for the coordinator discussed above because it is currently used in two senses: on the one hand the manager who is responsible for the licensing policy of his company (that is, the decision whether to "sell" or "buy" a licence in respect of a particular item of technology) and for the location of companies willing to "buy" or "sell" a licence as the case may be; and on the other hand the person who acts as the coordinator in the sense in which the word is used here.

In the author's view these functions are distinct in operation and require different kinds of qualifications. The first requires the businessman's type of background and experience, the second the professional outlook. The two kinds of capability may occasionally be combined in one and the same man, and such a person could fill both the roles of a "licensing executive", but it seems likely that the temperament, cast of mind and abilities of the businessman and the professional tend to be opposites and are not normally found in the same person. Certainly this is sufficiently often the case to make it desirable for a company to take account of the two functions and make a deliberate decision whether to combine them in one man or divide them between two. The choice in any particular case will depend largely on who is available, and it may be of assistance to note in this connection that the qualifications required for the coordinator correspond closely with those of the patent agent.

NEGOTIATIONS — THE RIGHT WAY

Given a coordinator, and assuming he is not the same person as the manager in charge of the particular licensing operation, the progress of negotiations from the initial location of an interest to the completion of the agreement could take the following form:

Stage 1 Manager *A* and Manager *B* discuss the broad terms and remit their views to their respective coordinators *A* and *B* in their own words, without attempting to write heads of agreement.

Stage 2 Coordinator *A* in discussion with Manager *A* formulates heads of agreement which will be adequate to enable Lawyer *A* to draft an agreement.

Estimated time: two weeks.

Stage 3 Either (*a*) the heads of agreement depart radically from what the managers initially agreed or (*b*) they do not.

If (*a*), Coordinator *A* arranges a meeting with Coordinator *B*, preferably with Managers *A* and *B* also present, to discuss and settle the revised broad terms as set out in *A*'s heads of agreement.

Estimated time: two weeks.

If (*b*), this step can be omitted.

Stage 4 Coordinator *A* gives the heads to Lawyer *A*, who is able to convert them into a draft agreement (Draft 1). This work is assisted by easy communication between the coordinator and lawyer. Allowing for this and some progressing by the coordinator, the time for preparing the draft may be estimated at one month.

Stage 5 At the same time as giving the heads to Lawyer *A*, Coordinator *A* consults Taxman *A* regarding the proposed financial provisions and, if necessary, refers back to Manager *A* to get them revised to overcome any tax difficulties. (There will not normally be any need to refer to *B* at this stage, though any change should be explained when sending *B* the draft agreement.) If necessary, Coordinator *A* arranges a meeting with Lawyer *A* and Taxman *A* before or after any consultation with Manager *A*. The coordinator will probably be able to fit in the consideration by the taxman before Lawyer *A* actually starts his drafting work, but to allow for eventualities, add a further two weeks.

Stage 6 Lawyer *A* gives Draft 1 to Coordinator *A* who immediately arranges a discussion with Lawyer *A* to go over the draft and make any alterations agreed between them. Reference to Manager *A* at this stage is unlikely to be necessary. Lawyer *A* produces revised draft (Draft 2).

Estimated time: two weeks.

Stage 7 Coordinator *A* sends Draft 2 to Coordinator *B*, with a copy to Manager *A*. Within *B* a similar process of consultation takes place and eventually Coordinator *B* secures a re-draft or amendments which result in Draft 3. This stage may be assisted by informal contact between the two coordinators.

Estimated time: six weeks.

Stage 8 Coordinator *B* sends Draft 3 to Coordinator *A* with a copy to Manager *B*, and the process of consultation within *A* is repeated. When this is concluded, Coordinator *A* arranges a meeting between the two teams *A* and *B* with a view to finally settling the draft.

The time between receipt of Draft 3 and the meeting may be estimated at six weeks.

Stage 9 The meeting takes place and the draft is settled over the table.

Stage 10 The draft as settled is engrossed by Lawyer *A* and executed by both parties. With progressing by the coordinators, the time for this may be reduced to two months.

The total time for this procedure works out at about seven to eight months. In addition, the result should be a better agreement, more truly reflecting the wishes of the parties. This is partly due to the improved consultation made possible by the bridging activity of the coordinators, but also because coordination by one individual introduces flexibility into the procedure. For example, not only are the initial heads of agreement more efficiently arrived at, but each coordinator can spot any point of substance, arising from any quarter during the process of negotiation, on which his colleagues would like to see a modification of the basic agreement as expressed in the heads. For example, further reflection and discussions with a director or other colleagues may convince Manager *A* that the provision for an annual minimum royalty is unsatisfactory, and that *A* would prefer to grant a non-exclusive licence without such provision.

Coordinator *A* can then extract this point for immediate discussion between Managers A and *B*, possibly without interrupting the overall procedure.

It should be noted here that in both schemes — coordinated and uncoordinated — the manager is considered as being the only person concerned at policy level in each company. In fact, he may need or wish to consult colleagues at the same or a higher level from time to time and this may (but not necessarily will) add some delay to the estimated time for either procedure.

INCOMPLETE AGREEMENTS

The negotiating procedures described above are intended to result in contracts which are complete in the legal sense of being fully enforceable in law. Situations can, however, arise in which such a contract is either unnecessary or not appropriate. These can be classified as situations in which an intention is expressed in order to enable the later stages of a negotiation to proceed; agreements which involve too many unknowns to enable the parties to make legally enforceable commitments in respect of some future eventuality; and situations where the commercial importance or value of the contract is too small to warrant the time and effort necessary to resolve all the issues which may arise between the parties.

Letters of intent

The sort of situation in which a letter of intent is appropriate is one in which one or both of the parties need to carry out a substantial investigation before they can commit themselves to the terms of an agreement. For example, a prospective licensee may need to undertake a market research project before deciding how much royalty he can agree to pay. In such a case he may seek a firm statement of the licensor's intention to grant him a licence. Such a statement, often called a letter of intent, would aim to give the prospective licensee sufficient confidence to incur the expense of the market research.

A letter of intent is not a contract and is not legally enforceable. It does, however, carry sanctions of the type referred to in Chapter 6 in connection with agreements for research into biological uses of chemical compounds and to that extent provides a basis for the other party's expenditure on his investigation.

Unknown factors

This latter type of agreement, as we saw, should ideally urgency and/or the value of the licence are such that they provide for the allocation between the parties of the benefits accruing if one of the compounds under assessment reaches the stage of commercial exploitation, but in practice there are too many unknown factors to enable this to be done. As a half-way house, therefore, the parties may negotiate certain criteria which will determine the terms of an agreement for allocating the benefit, and undertake each to use his best endeavours to negotiate such an agreement when the time comes. This, as explained in Chapter 6, is too indefinite to be enforceable in law, but it carries moral and social sanctions which may make it better than no agreement at all.

Incomplete agreements

If every agreement had to be drafted or scrutinised by the lawyers of each party, most of the smaller and/or more rapid transactions of business life would never get done. The size of the transaction or the speed with which it must be completed often contra-indicates such treatment, and one or both of the parties ignores the "fine print" on the basis that the likely cost of losing a dispute, taking into account the low probability of such a dispute arising, would not be great enough to make the employment of a lawyer worthwhile in terms of time or money. Of course the time factor is often decisive. If one is buying a railway ticket, one wants to complete the transaction in a few moments and therefore refrains from referring to one's lawyer the terms on which the railway accepts one as a passenger. Similarly in the case of licence agreements, there is no law which requires the parties to call in their lawyers if they feel that the commercial urgency and/or the value of the licence are such that they prefer not to do so. They can agree between themselves on the terms of the licence and if these terms are expressed with reasonable clarity they will have made an enforceable contract. The parties will incur a certain amount of risk by failing to take legal advice but provided they do so with their eyes open they may well in a particular case be justified. It is hoped that this book will have shown them the sort of risks involved and enabled them to make a sensible judgement.

THE NEGOTIATING MEETING

There are several processes at work in a negotiating meeting. If we assume a meeting comprising Managers *A* and *B*, Lawyers *A* and *B*, and Coordinators *A* and *B*, there will be a tendency for the managers to want to discuss the broad issues and to emphasise their community of interest; for the lawyers to deal with every point in detail and to allow for the conflicting interests of the parties; and for the coordinators to try to coordinate these different approaches. How the discussion proceeds will depend on the personalities of those present, particularly the chairman of the meeting. Such a meeting usually has before it a draft agreement and it is generally impracticable to proceed otherwise than by going through the draft. This at once plunges the meeting into an assortment of major, minor and purely drafting issues. If the chairman understands his job, he will try to steer the discussion so that priority is given to the major issues, making a note to return to the minor ones as he goes along. If time permits discussion of all the minor issues as well as the major ones, well and good. Failing this, any issues left over should be remitted to the coordinators to settle with the assistance of the lawyers, possibly at a later meeting which the managers need not attend.

If the "away" team has travelled a long way, it may be necessary to sit for some days in order to settle every issue at one time. Particularly is this so in the case of meetings in the USA. There will probably be an extensive "home" team and the American style requires particularly close attention to detail. The discussions will also be complicated by anti-trust considerations.

Content of discussion

This, at least as far as the managers are concerned, will be two-fold: to persuade the other side by argumentation, and to probe for information on which realistic proposals can be based. As pointed out earlier in this chapter, it is likely that most of the argumentation is a debating process in which the aim is to gain the psychological ascendancy. This can be illustrated by arguments on the rate of royalty.

A puts forward a figure of *x* per cent. In support of this he argues that the usual rate in this kind of business is a little above *x* and points out that the licensed product could easily stand *x* without diminishing sales. If *B* is to get *x* reduced to say $\frac{1}{2}(x + y)$ he must put forward a proposal for *y* per cent and successfully meet *A*'s arguments. He must be able to say convincingly that the going royalty rate in the business is markedly less than *x* (not greater as *A* contends) and that *x* would practically kill the market for the licensed product. (In countering this, *A* will probe *B* for market information.)

This kind of argument has much more to do with a battle of wits than with the objective information it is supposed to be dealing with. Thus, the standard rate of royalty is (*a*) probably non-existent, (*b*) not known if it does exist, (*c*) irrelevant. The rate of royalty which the product will bear is certainly relevant but is probably a purely relative matter. Thus, a royalty of *y* might reduce sales less than one of *x*, but it does not follow that *x* would not bring a greater return to the licensor. *B* tries to persuade *A* otherwise, but the basis of the argument is almost certainly subjective. Even with an established product a full-scale market research would be necessary to provide an objective basis, and the product in question is likely to be not yet on the market. The fact is that the "right" royalty for *A* to ask is the maximum which *B* will pay, and vice versa, and as far as objective fact is concerned, that is all there is to it.

Glossary

This glossary provides a ready reference for specialist terminology used in this book or which the reader may come across elsewhere in connection with licensing.

Where terms are used in different senses in the UK, the USA or the other principal English speaking countries, the different meanings are noted. Unless otherwise stated it may be assumed that Canadian usage follows that of the USA and Australian that of the UK. Many of the legal terms are different in Scotland, but the Scottish versions are not given here.

Abuse of Monopoly: Use of monopoly rights granted by a patent in such a way as to frustrate the purpose of securing exploitation of the invention by manufacture in this country.

Not used in the USA; nearest analogy is "Misuse of Patent".

Canada: "abuse of exclusive rights".

Anti-trust: USA. The system of US law which is directed against the formation of trusts or monopolies and the suppression of competition.

Corresponding Canadian term: Anti-combine.

Assign: To transfer the property, in for example, a patent, from the *assignor* to the *assignee;*
Assignment: (1) The act of assigning
(2) The deed or like document which effects the transfer of property.
Attorney: USA. A lawyer. May perform the function of an English solicitor or barrister or both.
Barrister: UK. Lawyer who is alone entitled to plead in Court. May also appear in Patent Office proceedings. Must be instructed by solicitor for former but may be instructed by patent agent for latter.
Breach: Failure by a party to an agreement to comply with its terms.
Break clause: Provision of an agreement permitting one or both parties to terminate it.
Claim: The clause (or one of the clauses) at the end of a patent specification which defines the "fenced-off" technological area which the Patentee can prevent others from entering.
Common Market Patent: The proposed patent which will cover the whole area of the Common Market (*see also* European Patent).
Compulsory licence: UK and Canada. A licence ordered to be granted by the Patent Office on the application of a person who successfully alleges an abuse of monopoly by the patentee.
No similar provision in USA.
Confidential information: Information imparted to a person on condition that he does not disclose it, or in circumstances from which such a condition may reasonably be inferred.
Consideration: The benefit or advantage which a party to an agreement receives (or which "flows" to him) from the other party.
Contract: (1) A legally enforceable relationship between two parties under which one party *A* gives, or promises to give, something to the other *B* in return for something given or promised by *B* to *A*.
(2) The document (usually formal) which gives effect to (1).

Convention, The: Abbreviation for The International Convention for the Protection of Industrial Property.

Convention application: UK. A patent application for an invention in respect of which an application had previously been filed within twelve months in another Convention country, and claiming priority from such earlier application under the provisions of the Convention.

Exists in the USA, but the term is not used.

Counsel: The advocate or body of advocates who plead(s) a client's case. In England, a commonly used term for a Barrister.

In USA, often used for an attorney specialising in advocacy.

Covenant: An undertaking forming part of a contract between *A* and *B* whereby *A* promises *B* to do or refrain from doing something.

Deed: A formal legal document.

Determine: To terminate an agreement or contract.

Dominant patent: If the area defined by the claim of a patent falls within the boundaries of the area defined by the claim of an earlier patent, the earlier patent is said to be dominant.

Synonymous with master patent.

E.E.C.: European Economic Community; synonymous with Common Market.

Europatent: A term sometimes used for Common Market Patent (qv); may also (incorrectly in the author's view) be used for European Patent (qv).

European Patent: The proposed patent which will be granted by the proposed European Patent Office but which will have effect as a separate patent in each of those countries belonging to the proposed European Patent Convention which have been "designated" by the applicant for the patent; thus a "bundle" of national patents.

European Patent Convention: The proposed treaty between most of the west European countries for setting up the European Patent Office which will administer the grant of European Patents.

Engrossment: Originally the formal document embodying the agreed text of a deed and written with the traditional law stationer's flourishes, ready for execution by the parties.

Nowadays may be used for any agreed legal text ready for execution, regardless of layout and style of writing. Hence the currently more usual term (especially in USA) "signature copy".

Exclusive licence: A licence under a patent which excludes others, even the patentee, from operating under the patent, either as a whole or as to a defined technological or (in theory) geographical area covered by the patent.

In the UK the exclusive licensee has a statutory status under the Patents Act 1949 which gives him most of the rights of the patentee.

First refusal of a licence, etc: A term often used to denote an agreement between *A* and *B* under which *A* promises not to grant, for example, a licence to a third party *C*, (1) without first having made an offer to *B*, and (2) on terms more favourable to *C* than were offered to *B*.

B is then said to have "first refusal" of the licence.

Heads of agreement: A statement of the proposed main terms of an agreement.

Improvement: Among those who mistakenly believe that the word has a special legal significance, this is generally regarded as meaning an improvement of a patented invention which falls within the defined boundary of the technological area covered ("claimed") by the Patent.

(If this or any other special sense is meant in an agreement, it should be clearly stated.)

Infringement of a patent or registered trade mark: To do something which is within the monopoly rights granted by the patent or registration. Thus, to "infringe a patent" (sometimes wrongly stated as to infringe *on* a patent).

Interference: USA. A proceeding peculiar to the USA for determining the priority as between applicants with co-pending applications for patents for the same invention. The priority is allotted to the person who ranks (according to a complex set of criteria) as the first inventor.

Canadian law has an analogous procedure known as a "conflict".

(In all other countries the priority is allotted, by and large, to the first person to file his patent application at the relevant Patent Office.)

International Convention: See Convention, The.

Invention: (1) A new article or product or industrial process of the kind on which a patent can be based.

(2) The technological area defined by the claims of a patent; thus "the invention claimed by a patent".

(In this book the word is used only in sense (1).)

Issue a writ: UK. To start a civil action — for example, for infringement of a patent — in the High Court.

Issue of a Patent: USA. The grant of a patent.

Know-how: Probably originally intended to mean that part of the technical information on a product or process which had not been reduced to writing or drawing.

Now often used more generally to mean any confidential technical information of industrial significance; and so used in this book.

Some of those, especially in USA, who use the term in the more general sense are beginning to use the term "show-how" for know-how in its original, more restricted, sense.

Letter of intent: A letter from *A* to *B* setting out *A*'s intention to enter into a contract with *B*, the purpose of which is to encourage *B* to take preliminary steps which will lead to negotiation and conclusion of the contract, or may even anticipate the conclusion of the contract.

Letters patent: Open letter from the Sovereign conveying the grant of a privilege; hence an abbreviation for "letters patent for an invention". In this sense synonymous with "patent", but still often used in licence agreements and so on. Has the drafting advantage of standing for both the singular (patent) and plural (patents).

Licence, Patent: Permission granted by the patentee to the licensee to work within the technological area defined by the claims of the patent.

In USA, spelt "license".

Licence, Trade-mark: Permission to use a trade mark, whether registered or not.

Licence, Know-how: Permission which is given by *A* to *B* explicitly or implicitly to use know-how (with or without restrictions) as a condition of the disclosure of the know-how by *A* to *B*, and its acceptance by *B*.

License, to: To grant a licence.

Also generally used in the USA and to a growing extent in UK to mean also "to *take* a licence." (In the author's view this use of the word in diametrically opposite senses is confusing and unnecessary; like using the same word for "buy" and "sell".)

License-in: To take a licence.

License-out: To license.

Licences-of-right: UK. Endorsement of a patent which has the effect (1) of obliging the patentee to grant a licence to any person requesting one, the terms to be settled by the Comptroller of Patents in the event of failure to agree; (2) of excusing the patentee half the annual renewal fees on the patent.

Not used in the USA.

Master patent: See Dominant patent.

Misuse of patent: US analogy of abuse of monopoly (qv).

Monopolies Commission: UK. Commission charged with administering the Monopolies Acts.

Most-favoured licensee terms: The provision in a licence agreement whereby the licensor undertakes not to grant a licence to a third party on terms more favourable to the third party than those of the existing licence are to the existing licensee.

Often referred to as "most-favoured nation terms" by analogy with tariff agreements between nations.

National Research Development Corporation (NRDC): UK. A corporation set up by the Development of Inventions Act 1948 for developing and exploiting inventions derived from certain sources or in certain categories.

No US equivalent. Canadian analogy: Canadian Patents and Developments Ltd.

No-contest clause: USA. The provision in a patent licence agreement whereby the licensee undertakes not to contest the validity of the patent.

Opposition: UK. Proceedings at the Patent Office whereby the opponent seeks refusal of the grant of a patent.

No US counterpart.

Option agreement: An agreement between *A* and *B* under which *B* has the option at some future time of adopting one of two alternative courses of action which are defined in the option agreement. For example, an option to take or decline a licence on terms specified in the option agreement. A "licence" under a patent application is in effect often an option to take a licence when the patent is granted.

Patent: (1) A monopoly right granted in respect of an invention to the inventor or his assignee.

(2) The documentary instrument issued to the patentee as a certificate of his title; sometimes known as the "letters patent document" or the "title deed".

The term patent is often used to denote a different entity: the patent specification. This usage is universal in the USA and common in the UK.

The term patent is also often used to denote an application for a patent or "patent application".

(In the author's view these two elliptical uses of the word patent are unfortunate as they can lead to inaccurate thinking and they have been avoided in this book.)

Patent agent: UK. A person who has been entered on the Register of Patent Agents maintained by the Chartered Institute of Patent Agents on behalf of the Department of Trade and Industry, by virtue of having passed the Intermediate and Final examinations administered by the Institute.

In the USA a person with a limited qualification entitling him to practise at the US Patent Office (*see* patent attorney).

Patent attorney: USA and Canada. A lawyer or attorney having in addition a US Patent Agent's qualification, and specialising in practice at the Patent Office and in patent law generally.

In Australia, the equivalent of the UK patent agent.

Patent Cooperation Treaty (PCT): A treaty recently signed by all the important countries of the world, but not yet in force, for a system administered by WIPO (qv) for the filing of a single patent application which will be subject to a single search but will become effective as separate applications in the countries "designated" by the applicant.

Patentee: The person entered in the Register of Patents as the owner of the patent.

Patent specification: USA. A document initially forming part of a patent application which describes the invention

Bibliography

The class of readers for whom this book is primarily intended are not likely to read much further into the subject. However, a few selected references may be useful.

Authoritative texts on industrial property law

KERLY, D M: *Kerly's Law of Trade Marks and Trade Names*, ninth edition by T A Blanco White, London, Sweet & Maxwell, 1966.
TERRELL, T: *Terrell on the Law of Patents*, twelfth edition by D Falconer, W Aldous and D Young, London, Sweet & Maxwell, 1971.
TURNER, A: *The Law of Trade Secrets*, London, Sweet & Maxwell, 1962.
WHITE, T A Blanco: *Patents for Inventions and the Registration of Industrial Designs*, third edition, London, Sweet & Maxwell, 1962.

Practitioner's books on licensing

These, especially in the UK, tend to be centred on "precedents" — that is, actual forms of words which have been used or recommended for licence agreements, and are known as "forms" in the USA.

A more general and also very comprehensive US book not confined to US law is:

COSTNER, Thomas E: *Patent Licensing Transactions*, New York, Matthew Bender, 1970.

Books mainly of precedents or forms are:

British

MELVILLE, L W: *Precedents on Industrial Property and Commercial Choses in Action*, London, Sweet & Maxwell, 1965.

Butterworth's Encyclopaedia of Precedents relating to Patents, Designs and Know-how: edited by D Fletcher Rogers.

US

NORDHOUS, Raymond C: *Patent Licensing Agreements, Law and Forms*, Chicago, Jural Publishing Co, 1967.

Restraints on licensing

US Anti-trust law It is difficult to suggest a book limited to misuse of patents and the anti-trust law of industrial property licensing, though the following "casebook" prepared for a law school course may be mentioned:

SHUR, Henry: *Patent Enforcement, Misuse and Anti-trust (Cases and Materials)*, Washington DC, Lerner Law Book Co Inc, 1967.

A most useful reference is:

Antitrust Developments 1955-68 (Chapter V), prepared by the Section of Antitrust Law of the American Bar Association,with annual supplements.

Common Market The difficulty here is to keep up to date with a rapidly moving subject. A specialist book on the industrial property aspects, published some years ago but giving the fundamentals of the subject is:

LEWIS, A K and KEMP, J A: *Registration of Commercial and Licence Agreements in the Common Market*, London, Butterworth & Co, 1962.

A more general book published in 1970 with a section on industrial property is:

ZAPHIRIOU, G A: *European Business Law*, London, Sweet & Maxwell, 1970.

Non-specialist books

CROPP, J A D, HARRIS, D C and STERN, E S: *Trade in Innovation — The Ins and Outs of Licensing*, London, Wiley, 1970.

BAXTER, J W: *World Patent Law and Practice*, London, Sweet & Maxwell, 1968.

Checklists

The British Institute of Management publishes a *Checklist on Licensing*. Alternatively the reader may prefer to use the list at the beginning of Chapter 4 of the present book for this purpose. In any event care should be taken not to regard a checklist as a substitute for approaching each agreement afresh on the basis of its own particular situation.

Case history

A full account of a classical licensing situation appears in: "The Eccentric Lords of Float Glass", *Fortune*, 1968, page 110.

Index